INTERACTIVE CITATION WORKBOOK FOR
ALWD GUIDE TO LEGAL CITATION

INTERACTIVE CITATION WORKBOOK FOR *ALWD GUIDE TO LEGAL CITATION*

2020 Edition

Jeffrey D. Jackson
Professor of Law
Washburn University School of Law

ISBN: 978–1–5221–8556–7

ISSN: 1932-1899

NOTE TO USERS

To ensure that you are using the latest materials available in this area, please be sure to periodically check the LexisNexis Law School web site for downloadable updates and supplements at www.lexisnexis.com/lawschool.

Editorial Office
230 Park Ave., 7th Floor, New York, NY 10169 (800) 543-6862
www.lexisnexis.com

MATTHEW◊BENDER

(7/2020–Pub.3146)

Table of Contents

Table of Contents

Acknowledgments

It takes a village to create the ICW! The ICW is made possible by the tremendous support we receive from our families, friends, research assistants, secretaries and law schools. Specifically, we would like to thank Touro Law Center, University of Illinois College of Law, and Washburn University, and of course, our first-year law students.

Using the Interactive Citation Workbook

Layout of the Workbook

The ICW contains seventeen citation exercises. Each exercise builds on and reinforces the skills learned in previous exercises. The goal of this learning method is for you to become familiar with the organization and use of the *ALWD* (pronounced "Allwood") *Guide to Legal Citation.**

You need not memorize the citation rules. However, through repeated use, you will probably find that you have memorized the commonly-used rules.

Each ICW chapter consists of explanatory text and a citation exercise. The text will introduce and explain the rules needed for that exercise, demonstrate by example how those rules are used, and give a checklist you can use in drafting your citations for that exercise. Because each exercise builds on previous exercises, you might find each checklist helpful for many of the later exercises as well. The exercises may be completed in the Workbook and turned in, or you may transfer your answers to the Workstation for immediate feedback. Check with your instructor to see which method you should use.

Beginning to Use the *ALWD Guide*

The *ALWD Guide* is divided into several major sections. To help you navigate it more easily, you may want to tab the sections of the *ALWD Guide* you will use most: Citation Basics, Cases, Statutes, Appendix 1, Appendix 2, Appendix 3, Appendix 4, Appendix 5, and the Index. Before you begin any ICW exercises, you should read the Introductory Material section. Pay particular attention to the section titled "How to Use The *ALWD Guide*." Although the index gets only a one-sentence mention, it can be tremendously helpful to you. If you have a question about drafting a citation, and you have no idea where to start, the index is your best bet.

The *ALWD Guide* is currently in its Sixth Edition.

A Word about Print vs. Electronic Sources

Each year the legal profession moves away from researching dusty volumes in corners of law libraries to paperless research online. Many (if not most) cases, statutes, legislative history documents, and secondary sources that are available in print are also available through electronic databases or on the Internet. Not only have commercial electronic databases such as Westlaw and Lexis Advance become standard tools of the trade at many, if not most, law firms, but also Internet websites hosted by governmental or commercial entities have become numerous and easy to use. Rules 30 and 32 walk us through the proper citation forms for the various alternative sources to primary and secondary legal materials. In addition, Rules 31 and 33 contains citation forms for resources that were never in print but have become very accessible to the public: blogs, podcasts, and videos, to name a few.

The *ALWD Guide* continues to prefer that legal writers cite to traditional printed sources for reasons of broad accessibility, authoritativeness, and permanence. Therefore, Rule 30 requires

---

* Excerpts from the *ALWD Guide to Legal Citation* used with permission of the copyright holders: The Association of Legal Writing Directors.

citations to traditional printed sources when available. However, the *ALWD Guide* does recognize that sometimes sources will only be found in nonprint sources or will be much easier to access using a nonprint source. Because our ultimate goal is to enable our reader to easily access the source using the information in our citation, Rule 30 allows citation to a digital copy, either as the only citation or as a supplement to a print source citation.

When appropriate, the chapters that follow will include instruction on both print and electronic sources, and those exercises will allow you to practice both print and electronic citations.

Getting the Most from the ICW

The Interactive Citation Workbook and Workstation (both "ICW") will help you learn the citation rules you will use most frequently when you clerk for a law firm or a court and, later, practice law. The ICW does not cover the rules that most practitioners rarely, if ever, use. However, after completing the ICW exercises, you should be comfortable enough with the *ALWD Guide* as a reference guide that you can find rules you need to cite any authority.

Legal citation has specific requirements for typeface. Those requirements are found in Rule 1.1. Although Rule 1.1 allows for italics as either *slanted type* or underlining, the ICW provides for only *slanted type*. Punctuation in combination with italicized material should be italicized according to Rule 1.3. In addition to typeface requirements, citation has specific spacing requirements. Those requirements are found in Rule 2.2.

Students are often eager to "jump in" and complete the online exercises, skipping either the workbook text or the *ALWD Guide* rules. However, because many of the examples in the workbook and the *ALWD Guide* are similar to the online problems, students often find that reviewing examples is faster than going it alone.

Students who have the most success with the ICW follow these steps:

- Read the rules identified at the beginning of each workbook chapter.

- Read the workbook chapter.

- Complete the exercise with both the workbook and the *ALWD Guide* at hand.

- Use the ICW hints to find the rule needed to correct incorrect citations (often the ICW problems will be similar to an example found in the *ALWD Guide*).

Using the New ICW Platform

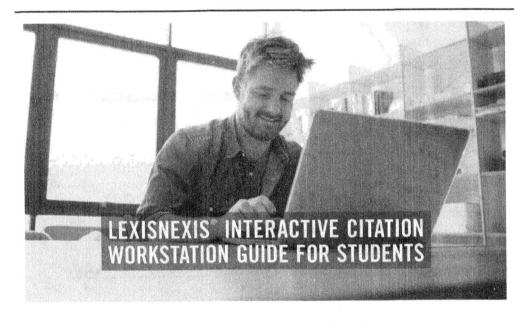

LEXISNEXIS® INTERACTIVE CITATION WORKSTATION GUIDE FOR STUDENTS

Efficiently sharpen and test your citation skills and become familiar with the organization and use of either *The Bluebook: A Uniform System of Citation®* or *ALWD Guide to Legal Citation*. Your instructor follows your progress as you complete problems, while ICW builds on and reinforces the skills you learned in previous exercises.

Accessing ICW

Step 1: Go to www.lexisnexis.com/lawschool and sign in using your LexisNexis® ID and password. That will bring you to the LexisNexis® Law School Home Page.

Step 2: Click on **Go To Lexis Advance®**.

Step 3: At the top left, click on **Lexis Advance® Research** and the downward facing arrow (v).

Step 4: Choose Lexis® Interactive Citation Workstation from the pull-down menu.

 LexisNexis®

Assigning Instructors

Step 1a: The very first time you enroll, a Welcome window will pop up. Click on **Go to Settings** to assign your course instructors.

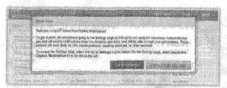

Or Step 1b: If you click **Close, I'll do this later**, you can add your instructors in Settings on your dashboard:

Step 2: On the Settings page, choose Lexis® Interactive Citation Workstation from the menu on the left.

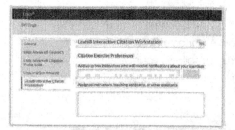

Step 3: Begin typing your instructor's last name, then choose the correct option from the list that appears. Click **Add**, then click **Save Changes** and Close.

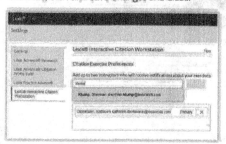

Completing an Exercise

1. Complete any or all problems within each exercise or only the ones your instructor has assigned. Your progress is shown on the left side in the progress bar. The default for each problem in ICW is three attempts, but your professor can change this from 1 to 5 attempts.

2. Use the textbox to enter your citation attempt. The textbox also has specific formatting features that include Bold, Italics, Small Caps, the section symbol and the paragraph symbol.

3. After you have entered your attempt in the text box, click on **Submit Answer**.

Submit Answer

4. When you are done with all of the problems you were assigned for an exercise, and you are ready to send your results to your instructor, click on **Complete Exercise**.

Complete Exercise

Viewing Your Results

1. The ICW dashboard provides a snapshot of your progress across all exercises and includes the last access date and time to help you meet assigned deadlines.

ALWD Exercises	
1: CASE NAMES	Not Started
2: CASE LOCATION	Not Started
3: COURT & DATE	Not Started
4: PARALLEL CITATIONS	Not Started
5: SHORT FORMS (CASES)	Not Started
6: FEDERAL STATUTES	Not Started
7: STATE STATUTES	In Progress: Dec 09, 2014 11:23:11 a.m. EST
8: SHORT FORMS (STATUTES)	Not Started
9: COMPREHENSIVE CORE EXERCISE	Not Started
10: PRIOR & SUBSEQUENT CASE HISTORY	Not Started
11: SECONDARY SOURCES	Completed: Dec 16, 2014 03:03:55 p.m. EST
12: PARENTHETICALS	In Progress: Dec 09, 2014 11:29:05 a.m. EST
13: SIGNALS	Not Started
14: LEGISLATIVE HISTORY	Not Started
14: ADMINISTRATIVE RESOURCES	Not Started
15: ELECTRONIC, INTERNET & NONPRINT SOURCES	Not Started
16: WHEN DO I CITE?	Not Started
17: COURT DOCUMENTS: TRIAL & APPELLATE	Not Started
View more details	

2. Click on **View more details** to see additional information regarding your progress for each exercise, including the number of correct, incorrect or remaining problems you have to complete.

3. You may also review the completion certificate for an individual exercise either in the dashboard view under Actions or in the individual exercise.

4. A link to your completion certificate will be sent to your assigned instructors upon completion (as long as you have assigned instructors in Settings). You may also send to others or download for your files by using the delivery options at the top of the screen. This includes the ability to Save to a Folder, Print, Download or Email the document..

Requesting a Reset

You have several ways to request a reset of a completed exercise. In the individual exercise, there is an option to reset:

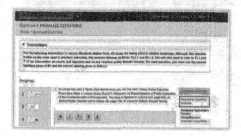

Or in the dashboard under **View more details** you can make this request in Actions:

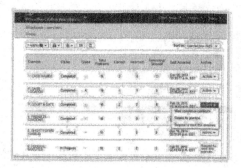

Questions? Send us an email using the student dashboard.

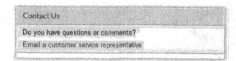

or contact us at **1-800-45-LEXIS**.

Interactive Citation Workstation

It is strongly recommended that students use the Interactive Citation Workbooks to accompany their work on the Interactive Citation Workstation. These workbooks are available for sale on the LexisNexis Store in eBook or print. Students may purchase the workbook via the Dashboard.

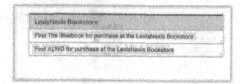

Need help?

For additional information about ICW, please click on **More** in the upper-right corner and then click on **Help** in the pull-down menu:

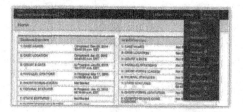

Various topics are covered in this section to help assist you in using ICW.

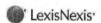

LexisNexis·

Chapter 1

CASE NAMES

Legal citation, like citation in other disciplines, identifies the source of an idea that a writer uses in his or her writing. A legal citation to a judicial opinion (a "case") has three basic components, all of which are given in the heading of every judicial opinion: the case name, the volume and page number of the source the opinion is printed in (the "reporter"), and a parenthetical that includes the identification of the court that issued the opinion and the date of the opinion. The first three exercises of the ICW will acquaint you with how to use the information given in the heading of an opinion to draft a basic legal citation. As you read the text in each ICW chapter, you may find it helpful to refer to the *ALWD* rules mentioned so you can familiarize yourself with both the content and location of the rules. Also, the examples provided in the *ALWD Guide* following each rule will be helpful in understanding the rule itself.

The "formula" for a basic legal citation follows:

Party 1 v. Party 2, Vol. Reporter Pg. (Court Date).

A. USING TYPEFACE

The first part of a citation is the case name (*Party 1 v. Party 2*). The case name is made up of the names of the parties. Looking at the citation formula above, you will notice that the case name (*Party 1 v. Party 2*) is italicized. This follows *ALWD* Rules 1.1 and 1.3, which allow for either *italicizing* or underlining the entire case name. When you type your citations in the ICW, you will use italics. Otherwise, you should check with your instructor or supervising attorney for his or her preference. What you might not notice at first glance is that the comma following the case name is *not* italicized. This follows Rule 1.3, which tells you not to italicize punctuation when it *follows* italicized material. Italicize punctuation only if it is *within* the italicized material.

B. SHORTENING PARTY INFORMATION

The party information is given at the beginning of a court opinion in the heading. You should list parties in the order they are given in the heading, regardless of procedural posture (*e.g.*, if the defendant is listed first in the heading, list him or her first in the citation). Because cases may involve multiple parties, one or more of which may have a lengthy name, the *ALWD Guide* provides a system of rules for shortening the case name so that the citation to an opinion is not cumbersome, yet still sufficiently identifies the primary parties. These rules are found in 12.2 with some additional guidance on abbreviations coming from Appendix 3 in the back of the *ALWD Guide*.

The rules in 12.2 fall into two general categories: rules calling for omissions and rules calling for abbreviations. Read these rules carefully before attempting the Case Names exercise.

You **should omit** the following general types of information from the citation:

- any actions other than the first in a consolidated case (12.2(b))
- any parties other than the first listed on each side (12.2(c))
- phrases indicating multiple parties (12.2(c))
- descriptive terms (12.2(c)) or official titles (12.2(m)) for parties identified by name
- abbreviations such as "d/b/a" following business names (12.2(e)(2))
- given names or initials of *individuals* (12.2(d)(1)), but not in the name of a business (12.2(e)(2))
- "State of," "Commonwealth of," and "People of," unless the party name is the same as the state the opinion is from. In that case, use only "State," "Commonwealth," or "People" (12.2(i))[1]
- the name of the Commissioner of Internal Revenue (12.2(l))
- all but the first-listed piece of property when property is a party (12.2(n))
- "The" as the first word in a party name (12.2(r))
- the second business designation when a name includes two or more business designations (12.2(e)(1))
- longer geographical references when a city or municipality is a party (12.2(j))

You **should abbreviate** words in a citation in the following circumstances:

- "versus" to "v." (12.2(c))
- "the United States of America" to "United States" (12.2(h))
- "Commissioner of Internal Revenue" to "Comm'r" (12.2(l))
- relator information to "ex rel." (12.2(o))
- procedural phrases (12.2(p))
- any word of an organization's name listed in Appendix 3 (12.2(e)(2)), including the first word in an organization's name[2]
- a party name to widely-recognized initials (12.2(e)(3))

You **should not abbreviate** the following:

- any word not listed in Appendix 3
- any word not listed in Rules 2.3 and 12.2(e)(3) *if the citation is used as a part of speech in a textual sentence.*

When drafting a case name, first omit the necessary information and then abbreviate the rest. Let's try an example of a case name in a citation sentence and then in a textual sentence before you tackle the Case Names exercise.

---

[1] For governmental entities whose names are given as "The People of the State of" or "The Commonwealth of the State of," use "People" and "Commonwealth" respectively.

[2] The Sixth Edition of the ALWD Guide contains a misprint that reads "Do no abbreviate the first word in an organization's name." This is corrected in the online "Updates" page and in the examples in the ALWD Guide.

Southwest Engineering Company and John Doe, Defendants-Appellants, versus United States of America, Plaintiff-Appellee

First, let's **omit** all information that the rules require. Rule 12.2(c) requires that we omit all parties other than the first; so we will omit "and John Doe" from the first party:

Southwest Engineering Company ~~and John Doe~~, Defendants-Appellants, versus United States of America, Plaintiff-Appellee

Rule 12.2(c) also requires that we omit descriptive terms for named parties, so we will delete "Defendants-Appellants" and "Plaintiff-Appellee":

Southwest Engineering Company ~~and John Doe, Defendants-Appellants~~, versus The United States of America, ~~Plaintiff-Appellee~~

Rule 12.2(h) requires that we cite "The United States of America" as "United States":

Southwest Engineering Company ~~and John Doe, Defendants-Appellants~~, versus United States, ~~Plaintiff-Appellee~~

Now that we have omitted all of the words *ALWD* requires, let's **abbreviate** what's left. First, we abbreviate "versus" to "v." following Rule 12.2(c).

Southwest Engineering Company ~~and John Doe, Defendants-Appellants~~, v. United States, ~~Plaintiff-Appellee~~

Then, we look in Appendix 3 to see which words in "Southwest Engineering Company" should be abbreviated. We notice that all three words are listed in Appendix 3; so we abbreviate those words:

Sw. Eng'g Co. ~~and John Doe, Defendants-Appellants~~, v. United States, ~~Plaintiff-Appellee~~

Now, all we have to do is italicize the case name, and it's ready to take its place in a citation sentence!

Sw. Eng'g Co. v. United States

But what if we wanted to use this case name in a textual sentence? Rules 2.3 and 12.2(e)(3) tell us that, in a textual sentence, we only abbreviate the words in a case name that are listed in Rule 2.3's Chart 2.1 or in 12.2(e)(3) regardless of whether other words are listed in Appendix 3. Neither "Southwest" nor "Engineering" is on the 2.3 or 12.2(e)(3) "short list." However, "Company" is. Therefore, if we wanted to use this case name in a textual sentence, it would look like this:

Southwest Engineering Co. v. United States

CHECKLIST FOR CASE NAMES

- Have you italicized the case name?
- Have you omitted words according to 12.2?
  - additional parties or actions
  - given names or initials of individuals
  - geographical terms and locations as necessary
  - surplus business designation names
  - surplus pieces of property
- Have you abbreviated words according to 12.2?
  - "versus" to "v."
  - "the United States of America" to "United States"
  - "Commissioner of Internal Revenue" to "Comm'r"
  - relator information to "ex rel."
  - procedural phrases
  - words listed in Appendix 3
  - an organization name to widely-recognized initials

Exercise 1
CASE NAMES

Put the following case name information in correct *ALWD* citation form. All cases are being cited in citation sentences unless the problem indicates otherwise. This exercise focuses on Rule 12. If the *ALWD Manual* allows for an abbreviation or omission, the correct answer on the ICW will incorporate that abbreviation or omission, except where the resulting abbreviation would consist of only one letter that would leave the reader in doubt as to what the abbreviation refers, and thus would have the potential to cause confusion. In such a case, the correct answer will use the entire word.

1. A consolidated action styled Frank Messina v. William W. Burden; Leonard Armstrong v. Dennis R. Johnson

_____

_____

2. C.A. Nelson, appellee, versus the City of Las Vegas, appellant

_____

_____

3. The Estate of Jim Johnson

_____

_____

4. Eleanor and Kenneth Buskirk, petitioners, versus Carey Canadian Mines, Limited, respondent

_____

_____

5. Sabine Pilot Services, Incorporated, appellant, versus Michael Andrew Hauck, appellee

_____

_____

6. New York Times Company versus L.B. Sullivan

_____

_____

7. A Texas Court of Criminal Appeals case, The State of Texas versus Robert Earl Johnson

_____

_____

8. South Dakota Department of Health versus Tony Heim

_____

9. In the Matter of Guardian Casualty Company, Incorporated

_____

10. Tex Smith d/b/a The Harmonica Man versus Arthur Godfrey, et al.

_____

11. A federal case from the Eastern District of Missouri, The State of Missouri ex
     rel. Wear versus Springfield Gas & Electric Company, Incorporated

_____

12. American Exchange Bank of Madison, Wisconsin versus The United States of
     America

_____

13. A United States Supreme Court case, South Dakota, petitioner, versus Elizabeth
     H. Dole, Secretary, United States Department of Transportation

_____

14. Columbia Broadcasting System, petitioner, versus The Democratic National
     Committee, respondent [Hint: Columbia Broadcasting System is the television
     network CBS and is commonly referred to by its initials.]

_____

15. Helen Palsgraf, appellant, versus The Long Island Railroad Company, appellee

_____

Chapter 2

CASE LOCATION

Now that you know how to begin your legal case citation with the proper case name, you are ready to tackle the second major part of the citation: the case location information. Currently, the most commonly used location information for a case is the case's location in a reporter. In that case, the citation "formula" is one you are already familiar with:

Party 1 v. Party 2, Vol. Reporter Pg. (Court Date).

However, some jurisdictions have adopted location information that references the year of the decision and a number assigned to the case by the court that issued the opinion. That citation format is called "public domain citation." public domain citations use this formula:

Party 1 v. Party 2, Year COURT No., Vol. Reporter Pg.

You may or may not be able to tell that the comma following the case name in each formula is not italicized. Rule 1.3 tells us to italicize commas that are *within* italicized material but not those that *follow* italicized material. Because the comma after a case name follows italicized material, it is not italicized.

A. REPORTERS

A "reporter" is a compilation of judicial opinions, or cases. The compilation may be by jurisdiction (*e.g.*, *Florida Reports*) or by subject matter (*e.g.*, *Education Law Reporter*). A given case will be published in the reporter or reporters for that case's jurisdiction and may also appear in a subject matter reporter that contains other cases with the same topic. Legal citation, however, references only jurisdictional reporters.

Jurisdictional reporters may be either official publications authorized by statutes of the state or federal government or unofficial publications, often by private publishers. Both official and unofficial reporters are printed in series. Generally, reporter publishers will begin a new series rather than allow the volume numbers to exceed three digits. Therefore, after volume 999 of *South Western Reporter*, Second Series, the publisher next published volume 1 of *South Western Reporter*, Third Series.

State court cases are published in both state and regional reporters. State reporters may be official or unofficial and contain cases from only one state. Regional reporters are unofficial reporters published by West Group. These reporters contain state court cases from several states. For example, *Southern Reporter* publishes state court cases from Alabama, Florida, Louisiana, and Mississippi.

Federal cases are published in jurisdictional reporters by level of court. Federal district court cases are published in *Federal Supplement*. Federal courts of appeals cases are published in *Federal Reporter*. United States Supreme Court cases are published in three reporters: *United States Reports* (official), *Supreme Court Reporter* (unofficial), and *Lawyers' Edition* (unofficial).

Rules 12.3, 12.4, and 12.5 tell us that a citation must include a volume designation, the abbreviated name of the reporter, and the page on which the opinion begins in the reporter. Appendix 1 of the *ALWD Guide* is a listing of information for each jurisdiction in the United States. The listing first gives state information organized alphabetically by state name and then federal information. The first information given for each jurisdiction is the names of the courts in that jurisdiction, the names of the reporters for each court, and the abbreviations for those reporters.

Placing the volume designation in the citation is straightforward. The volume number appears on the spine of the reporter, and that number is the first information given in the case location portion of the citation.

Placing the reporter information in the citation requires a little more information. The abbreviation for the reporter is in the appropriate jurisdictional section of Appendix 1. Pay special attention to the spacing of the abbreviation. This spacing follows the rules given in 2.2. Rule 2.2 tells us to close up consecutive single capitals (*e.g.*, N.Y.). Ordinals (*e.g.*, 1st, 2d, 4th, etc.) are treated as single capitals (*e.g.*, S.W.2d). Longer abbreviations and single capitals adjacent to longer abbreviations should have a space between them (*e.g.*, Ala.^App. and F.^Supp.).[1] You can combine these spacing rules to handle both adjacent single capitals and longer abbreviations in the same reporter abbreviation (*e.g.*, N.C.^App.).

Finally, the number of the first page that the case appears on in the reporter follows the reporter abbreviation. When you give the reader the initial page number of the case, he or she has the information needed to find the case.

> *Hunter v. Gatherer*, 789 Rptr. 234 (Ct. 2002).

Sometimes, you will also want to direct your reader's attention to specific pages within the case. You can do this using a "pinpoint reference." Rules 12.5(b) and 5.2 say that you can pinpoint the location of specific information by following the initial page number in the citation with a comma, a space, and the page number containing the specific material. This specific page number is included *in addition to* the initial page number rather than as a substitute for it.

> *Hunter v. Gatherer*, 789 Rptr. 234, 237 (Ct. 2002).

If your pinpointed material spans more than one page, Rule 5.3 tells you to give the beginning and ending page numbers, separated by a hyphen or dash.

> *Tree v. Shrub*, 789 Rptr. 85, 87–89 (Ct. 2002).

If the page numbers contain more than two digits, Rule 5.3(b) tells us to drop Next, we add the court abbreviation for the

> *Hunter v. Gatherer*, 789 Rptr. 234, 237–39 (Ct. 2002).

---

[1] The caret symbol (^) in these examples shows the location of the space but would not actually be included in your citation.

Let's try an example to see how these rules work together. Say we have a Louisiana case called *Red v. Green*. *Red v. Green* is published in the Second Series of the *Southern Reporter*, volume 999, beginning on page 111. First, you know that the volume number goes first. It follows immediately after the case name, separated by a comma and a single space.

> *Red v. Green*, 999

Next comes the reporter. It has to be abbreviated, so we look under the jurisdiction of the case, "Louisiana," in Appendix 1 and find that *Southern Reporter* is abbreviated "So." or "So. 2d" depending on whether the case is printed in the First or Second Series. We know that our volume is in the Second Series, so "So. 2d" it is. Now we check Rule 2.2 to see the proper spacing to use in the abbreviation. "So." is not a single capital and "2d" is an ordinal treated as a single capital. Therefore, Rule 2.2(a) tells you to put a space between them.

> *Red v. Green*, 999 So. 2d

In many reporters, the header of each page contains a notation that reads "Cite as:" followed by the volume, reporter abbreviation, and page number of the case. While you can rely on the given volume and page number, be careful about relying on that header for the reporter abbreviation. The spacing in those abbreviations does not always conform to the *ALWD Guide*. For example, West's *Federal Supplement* headers give "F.Supp." as the appropriate abbreviation. However, Rule 2.2(c) requires a space between "F." and "Supp."

Back to our citation: All we lack is the beginning page number of the case. After we add that, the name and reporter elements of our citation are as follows:

> *Red v. Green*, 999 So. 2d 111

If we were citing to specific pages, 115 through 116, for example, in *Red v. Green*, they would follow the first page of the case. Remember, according to Rule 5.2, we add the specific page to our citation as a pinpoint reference after the page on which our case begins. Remember that when a pinpoint reference spans consecutive pages, you should include the first and last page numbers for the span, separated by a hyphen or dash. We then drop repetitious digits, but retain the last two digits for the ending page number. Then the name and reporter elements of our citation would be this:

> *Red v. Green*, 999 So. 2d 111, 115–16

B. CASES IN THE PUBLIC DOMAIN

Rule 12.11 provides an alternative to reporter citations. This alternative is called "public domain citation." Public domain citation format allows citation to the year of the decision, the court's abbreviation, the sequential number of the decision as assigned by the court issuing the opinion, and citation to a reporter.

> *Party 1 v. Party 2*, **Year COURT No., Vol. Reporter Pg.**

Although this is the formula suggested by Rule 12.11, individual states may prefer a different format. In that case, we follow that state's local rules for public domain citation.

By statute, South Dakota now requires that its public domain citations use the abbreviation "S.D." rather than the "SD" that both the ALWD Guide and the Bluebook list. Therefore, you should use "S.D." in answering any questions relating to public domain citations of South Dakota cases.

When a citation to a regional reporter is available, Rule 12.11 calls for a public domain citation *in addition* to a reporter citation. Otherwise, a public domain citation is used alone, without a reporter citation. To determine whether a state requires a public domain citation, consult that jurisdiction's information in Appendix 2. Although the *ALWD Guide* does not provide a pinpoint reference format for a public domain citation, local rules usually provide the format to be used with that state's opinions.

Drafting public domain citations is pretty simple. Let's say you want to cite *Orange v. Purple*, a North Dakota case decided in 1997. This was the ninety-sixth case decided in 1997 by the North Dakota Court of Appeals. The case is not included in *North Western Reporter*, the regional reporter that includes North Dakota state cases.

First, we look in Appendix 2 under "North Dakota" to see if North Dakota has adopted a public domain format. We find that, for cases decided after January 1, 1997, North Dakota has adopted the public domain citation format suggested by Rule 12.11. Therefore, we start with the year of decision:

> *Orange v. Purple*, 1997

Next, we add the court abbreviation for the North Dakota Court of Appeals. North Dakota local rules printed in Appendix 2 call for the North Dakota Courts of Appeals to be abbreviated in public domain citations as "ND App" (without periods).

> *Orange v. Purple*, 1997 ND App

Finally, we add the sequential number of the decision, 96. Because we do not need any more information to make this citation complete, we can place a period at the end of our citation sentence. Notice that this differs from reporter citations in that reporter citations require a court and date parenthetical before they are complete. (Chapter 3 introduces you to the court and date parenthetical.)

> *Orange v. Purple*, 1997 ND App 96.

If you wanted to direct your reader's attention to specific material, you could use a pinpoint reference as directed by the local rules. These rules allow for "spot cites" using the paragraph rather than page numbers of an opinion. Therefore, if the information you wanted to point out is found in the eleventh paragraph of the opinion, you would pinpoint this way:

> *Orange v. Purple*, 1997 ND App 96, ¶ 11.

Checklist for Print Reporters

- Have you put the volume number first?
- Have you abbreviated the reporter name as shown in Appendix 1?
- Have you closed up consecutive single capitals as shown in Rule 2.2?
- Have you given the first page of the case, even if there is also a pinpoint citation?
- Have you checked to make sure you have not put an extra space anywhere?

Checklist for Public Domain Citations

- Have you consulted Appendix 2 to see if the case's jurisdiction has adopted public domain citation? If it has, continue. If it has not, give a reporter citation rather than a public domain citation.
- Have you put the year of decision first?
- Have you given the court's abbreviation?
- Have you given the sequential number of the decision?
- If you need to direct your reader to specific material, have you included a pinpoint to the paragraph containing the material?
- Have you placed a period at the end of the citation?

Exercise 2
CASE LOCATION

Put the following case name and reporter information or public domain citation information in correct *ALWD* citation form. Do not put a period at the conclusion of the "citation" you draft if a court and the date parenthetical would be needed to complete the citation. All cases are being cited in a brief to be filed with the United States Supreme Court. Although this exercise builds on the rules used in the previous exercise, this exercise focuses on Rules 2.2, 12.3, 12.4, 12.5, and 12.11. You will also need to refer to Appendices 1 and 2 for information on reporter abbreviations and public domain citation requirements, as well as the internet resources listed there. If no public domain citation information is given, assume that none is available.

1. Susette Kelo, et al., Petitioners v. City of New London, Connecticut, et al., a United States Supreme Court case reported in volume 545, page 469, of *United States Reports*.

    _____

    _____

2. C.S. Moreland v. Chesapeake Stone Company, a Court of Appeals of Kentucky case reported in volume 104, page 762, of *Southwestern Reporter*.

    _____

    _____

3. 99 Cents Only Stores, a California corporation, versus Lancaster Redevelopment Agency, a public entity, and City of Lancaster, a public entity, a federal district court case published in volume 237, page 1123, of *Federal Supplement*, Second Series.

    _____

    _____

4. Frank E. Midkiff, Richard Lyman, Jr., Hung Wo Ching, Matsuo Takabuki and Myron B. Thompson, Trustees of the Kamehameha Schools/Bishop Estate, Plaintiff-Appellants, versus Paul A. Tom, Tony Taniguchi, Wilbert K. Eguchi, Wahne T. Takahashi, Commissioners of the Hawaii Housing Authority, Defendants-Appellants, a case decided by the United States Court of Appeals for the Ninth Circuit and reported in volume 702, page 788, of *Federal Reporter*, Second Series.

    _____

    _____

5. Michael J. Glick, D.D.S. versus Chocorua Forestlands Limited Partnership, a case decided by the Supreme Court of New Hampshire and reported in volume 949, page 693, of *Atlantic Reporter*, Second Series.

    _____

    _____

6. Nick F. Gyurkey, Plaintiff-Appellant, versus Lloyd Babler, Jr., Thomas Babler, Raymond A. Town, Jr., dba Western International Investors & Development Co., a case decided by the Supreme Court of Idaho and reported in volume 651, page 928, of *Pacific Reporter*.

    _____

    _____

7. Catherine Johnner versus Percy D. Mims, a case decided by the Supreme Court, Appellate Division, Second Department, of New York and reported in volume 850, page 786, of West's *New York Supplement*, Second Series.

    _____

    _____

8. Pacific Scene, Incorporated, v. Penasquitos, Incorporated, a case decided by the Supreme Court of California and reported in volume 250, page 651, of *California Reports*. [Note: This is not the same as *West's California Reporter*.]

    _____

    _____

9. Stacey Hildebrand, Plaintiff and Appellee, versus Shane Stoltz, Defendant and Appellant. This is a Supreme Court of North Dakota opinion issued as the 225th opinion of 2016.

    _____

    _____

10. Samantha Million, Plaintiff/Appellant versus Jay Scott Million, Defendant/Appellee. This is a Supreme Court of Oklahoma opinion issued as the 106th opinion of 2012. You do not wish to include the optional parallel citation. You wish to direct your reader's attention to specific material in paragraph 3 of the opinion.

    _____

    _____

Chapter 3

COURT & DATE

Congratulations! Now that you have mastered two major parts of a basic case citation, case names and case location, you are ready to learn the third and final portion of a case citation: the parenthetical containing the court deciding the case and the year of that decision. The court and date parenthetical appears immediately following the page information in your case citation. Now that you have constructed a full citation, you should end it with a period. A case citation used as a separate citation sentence, *i.e.*, not embedded in a textual sentence, should be punctuated as a sentence: Begin with a capital letter and end by placing a period after the court and date parenthetical. The general rules concerning this portion of the citation are Rules 12.6 and 12.7, so you should read these rules carefully before attempting Exercise 3.

Party 1 v. Party 2, Vol. Reporter Pg. (Court Date).

A. COURT INFORMATION

By looking at a case citation, your reader should be able to determine what court decided the case. In many citations, your reader will be able to make that determination from the reporter information because some official reporters publish only opinions of certain courts. In those citations, you will not include additional information in the court and date parenthetical. For example, *United States Reports* publishes only cases decided by the United States Supreme Court. Therefore, Rule 12.6(b) tells us that a cite to a case published in *United States Reports* can refer only to a United States Supreme Court case. Accordingly, you would not include additional information in the court and date parenthetical.

Boerne v. Flores, 521 U.S. 507 (1997).

1. State Cases

Some states have official reporters that publish only cases decided by a particular court in that state. For parallel citations with these reporters, Rule 12.6(d) provides that no additional information in the court and date parenthetical is necessary. For example, *South Dakota Reports* publishes only cases decided by the South Dakota Supreme Court. Therefore, a cite to a case published in *South Dakota Reports* would not include additional information in the court and date parenthetical because the reporter abbreviation, "S.D.," tells the reader that the South Dakota Supreme Court decided the case.

Landrum v. DeBruycker, 90 S.D. 304, 240 N.W.2d 119 (1976).

However, most reporters, particularly regional reporters, publish opinions from several different state courts. In each of those citations, you must include information telling your reader which court decided the case in question. Rule 12.6(a) and Appendix

15

1 assist us in formulating the abbreviation for each state court. For example, if you have a case from the Montana Supreme Court, you can look in the Montana entry in Appendix 1 and see that the abbreviation for that court appears in parentheses after the heading "Montana Supreme Court": "Mont." Because the reporter abbreviation "P.2d" does not indicate the court that decided this case, you would include that abbreviation in the court and date parenthetical.

> *State v. Ommundson*, 974 P.2d 620 (Mont. 1999).

Similarly, the *North Western Reporter* publishes cases decided by the highest and intermediate courts in seven different states. Therefore, if you are citing a Michigan Court of Appeals case and are citing to *North Western Reporter*, you would convey the court information to your reader in the court and date parenthetical. You would use the proper abbreviation for the Michigan Court of Appeals that is given in Appendix 1 in the parentheses following the heading "Michigan Court of Appeals": "Mich. Ct. App." (We will discuss when a writer needs to cite to a regional reporter and an official state reporter in connection with Exercise 4, Parallel Citations.)

> *Rutherford v. Chrysler Motors Corp.*, 231 N.W.2d 413 (Mich. Ct. App. 1975).

But wait, there's more! Some states publish an official reporter for cases from more than a single court, *e.g.*, from the supreme court and the appellate courts or from different departments or divisions within a certain court. If the name of the reporter tells your reader the name of the state but not the particular court or specific department or division, then you include the additional information in the court and date parenthetical, but omit the state information. For example, if you were going to cite to a New Mexico Court of Appeals case that was reported in *New Mexico Reports*, then you should omit the "N.M." portion of the correct abbreviation "N.M. Ct. App."

> *Lara v. City of Albuquerque*, 126 N.M. 455 (Ct. App. 1998).

As you might guess, you rarely will have citations like the above example; this situation occurs only when you have a state official reporter that publishes cases from more than one court or when you have a large state with divisions in the court system. Typically, if a state has an official reporter system, only supreme court cases are published or supreme court cases and courts of appeals cases are published in separate reporters. For instance, Washington has two official reporters; *Washington Reports* publishes opinions from the Washington Supreme Court, and *Washington Appellate Reports* publishes opinions from the Washington Court of Appeals.

2. Federal Cases

You must designate a court when citing to any federal case other than a Supreme Court case. The *Federal Reporter* publishes cases from each of the federal courts of appeals. The *Federal Supplement* publishes cases from each United States district court. If you have a case reported in the *Federal Reporter*, you can look under Appendix 4, "Court Abbreviations" and find the heading "United States Courts of Appeals." There you will find abbreviations for each of the circuit courts of appeals: 1st, 2d, 3d, 4th, 5th, 6th, 7th, 8th, 9th, 10th, 11th, D.C. Cir. and Fed. Cir.

> *Deus v. Allstate Ins. Co.*, 15 F.3d 506 (5th Cir. 1994).

Pay particular attention to cases decided by the Fifth Circuit in 1981 and 1982. The Fifth Circuit split into the Fifth and Eleventh Circuits on October 1, 1981. Rule 12.6(c) will give you guidance on whether you need additional information in your court and date parenthetical.

If you have a case reported in the *Federal Supplement*, you should look under the heading "United States District Courts" in Appendix 4. Appendix 4 lists the proper abbreviations for all the U.S. District Courts. In case of any confusion, remember that, according to Rule 2.2(a), adjacent capitals do not have spaces between them (S.D.N.Y.), but you must put a space between capitals and other abbreviations (D. Mass.).

Jones v. Clinton, 57 F. Supp. 2d 719 (E.D. Ark. 1999).

Bottom line: Your reader must be able to tell what court in what jurisdiction decided a certain case by looking at the citation. Whatever information the name of the reporter does not give, you must include in the court and date parenthetical.

B. DATE INFORMATION

Your reader also must be able to glean from your citation the date that your case was decided. Please note that the important date is the date the case was *decided*, not the date the case was *argued* or *heard*. For the majority of the cases that you cite, you will know what year the case was decided from reading the heading of the case in a reporter. For these cases, you simply include the year in the court and date parenthetical.

Stein v. Plainwell Community Schs., 822 F.2d 1406 (6th Cir. 1987).

Also, for cases that are not published in a reporter, you will need to include additional information besides the year of decision, according to Rule 12.7. For instance, if a case is not reported or is reported in a slip opinion or an electronic database, then you must give the exact date, *i.e.*, month, day, and year, of the decision. Note that Appendix 3 provides the proper abbreviations for the months of the year.

C. ELECTRONIC DATABASES

We have discussed how to cite to most print sources: cases we find in reporters, statutes we find in compilations, legislative history documents found in various government publications, and even common books, magazines, and newspapers. However, each year the legal profession moves away from researching dusty volumes in corners of law libraries to "paperless" research. Many (if not most) cases, statutes, legislative history documents, and secondary sources are also available through electronic databases or on the Internet. Not only have commercial electronic databases such as Westlaw and LexisNexis become standard tools of the trade at many, if not most, law firms, but also Internet websites hosted by governmental or commercial entities have become numerous and easy to use. Part 4 of the *ALWD Guide*, Chapters 30 through 33, walks us through the proper citation forms for the various alternative sources for primary and secondary legal materials. In addition, Rule 31 contains citation forms for websites, and Rule 33 even tells us how to cite to electronic mail.

The *ALWD Guide* states its preference that legal writers cite to traditional printed sources for reasons of broad accessibility, authoritativeness, and permanence. However, the *ALWD Guide* does recognize that sometimes sources will be found only in nonprint sources or will be much easier to access using a nonprint source. Because our ultimate goal is to enable our reader to easily access the source using the information in our citation, the authors warn us of the ephemeral nature of some Internet sites. Therefore, legal writers should remember to print out Internet materials and not trust that the source will be there tomorrow.

Rule 12.13 governs citation of cases found on commercial databases such as Bloomberg BNA, Lexis Advance, or WestlawNext. If a case is not published in a reporter, then you may cite to one of these commercial databases that does contain the case. You should include the following information:

- the case name,
- the docket number,
- the database identifier, which usually includes the year and the database abbreviation (LEXIS, WL), and a unique document number,
- the court name, and
- the full date of the decision.

Case Name, Docket Number, Database Identifier/Number (Court Month Day, Year).

State v. Werner, No. 96-8-00197-6, 1998 WL 283537 (Wash. Ct. App. June 2, 1998).

As with general case citation, if the database identifier is identical to the court abbreviation, then you do not repeat it in the court and date parenthetical.

Bush v. Gore, 2000 U.S. LEXIS 8430 (Dec. 12, 2000).

Notice that Rule 12.13 instructs you to include blanks for reporter information if the case will be printed in the reporter but has not yet been published.

If you wish to use a pinpoint citation to focus your reader's attention on a particular page, remember that the pages given in the reporter are not as useful on a computer screen. Commercial databases assign pages in a process called "star pagination." A pinpoint to one of these pages would contain the word "at" and then an asterisk and the page number, even in the long form of the citation.

Case Name, Docket Number, Database Name/Number **at *Pg** (Court Month Day, Year).

State v. Werner, No. 96-8-00197-6, 1998 WL 283537 at *2 (Wash. Ct. App. June 2, 1998).

The unique database identifier is retained in constructing a short form to a case found on an electronic database.

Werner, 1998 WL 283537 at *2.

Checklist for Court Information

- Are you citing from a federal reporter, a regional reporter, or a state reporter?

- If a federal reporter, but not *United States Reports*, have you included an abbreviation for the deciding court as shown in Appendix 4?

- If a regional reporter, have you included a full abbreviation for the deciding court as shown in Appendix 1?

- Does your state court have any division or department information that should be included?

- If a state reporter, does the state reporter publish opinions from any other court besides the deciding court?

- If the state reporter does publish opinions from more than one court, have you included an abbreviation for the deciding court as shown in Appendix 1? Do you need to include the part of the abbreviation designating the name of the state, or an you omit that information?

- Have you double-checked the spacing of your abbreviation according to Rule 2.2(a)?

Checklist for Date Information

- Is your case decided in a reporter? If so, have you included the year of decision in your citation?

- If your case is not reported in print, have you included the month, day, and year in your citation?

Exercise 3
COURT & DATE

Put the following information in correct *ALWD* citation form. All cases are being cited in citation sentences. Although this exercise builds on the rules used in the previous exercise, it focuses on Rules 12.6 and 12.7. You will also need to refer to Chart 12.2 for information on the reporters, and Appendices 1 and 4 for information on the abbreviations of courts and reporters containing cases from the appropriate jurisdiction. If the *ALWD Manual* allows for an abbreviation or omission, the correct answer on the ICW will incorporate that abbreviation or omission, except where the resulting abbreviation would consist of only one letter that would leave the reader in doubt as to what the abbreviation refers, and thus would have the potential to cause confusion. In such a case, the correct answer will use the entire word.

1. George Hawkins versus Edward R. B. McGee, a case from the Supreme Court of New Hampshire, decided June 4, 1929, and reported at volume 146, page 641, of *Atlantic Reporter*.

   _____

   _____

2. Willie Peevyhouse and Lucille Peevyhouse versus Garland Coal & Mining Company, a case decided by the Supreme Court of Oklahoma on December 11, 1962, and reported at volume 382, page 109, of *Pacific Reporter*, Second Series.

   _____

   _____

3. Steven Merola versus Exergen Corporation and Francesco Pompei, a case decided by the Appeals Court of Massachusetts on April 26, 1995, after argument on February 16, 1995, and reported at volume 648, page 1301, of *North Eastern Reporter*, Second Series.

   _____

   _____

4. Warner-Lambert Pharmaceutical Company, Incorporated versus John J. Reynolds, Incorporated, et al., a case decided by the United States District Court in the Southern District of New York on November 6, 1959, and reported at volume 178, page 655, of *Federal Supplement*.

   _____

   _____

5. Sally Beauty Company, Inc., versus Nexxus Products Company, Inc., a case decided by the United States Court of Appeals for the Seventh Circuit on September 26, 1986, and reported at volume 801, page 1001, of *Federal Reporter*, Second Series.

   _____

   _____

6.   Seaside Farm, Incorporated versus The United States of America, a case decided
     by the United States Court of Appeals for the Fourth Circuit on December 2,
     2016. It is an unpublished case. You found the case on Lexis Advance and wish to
     cite to that database. The unique database identifier is 2016 U.S. App. LEXIS
     21537. The docket number is 15-2562.

     _____

     _____

7.   Retirement Plans Committee, et al. versus Larry W. Jander, et al. This is a
     January 14, 2020 case from the United States Supreme Court. Assume this case
     has not yet been published in any reporter and you would, therefore, like to cite
     the slip opinion from the United States Supreme Court's web site at
     https://www.supremecourt.gov/opinions/19pdf/18-1165_4gcj.pdf/.   The   docket
     number for the case is 18-1165. You wish to direct the reader's attention to page 3
     of the slip opinion.

     _____

     _____

8.   General Utilities & Operating Company versus the Commissioner of Internal
     Revenue, Guy T. Helvering, a case decided by the United States Supreme Court
     in 1935 and reported at volume 296, page 200, of *United States Reports*.

     _____

     _____

9.   Marion E. Seaver versus Matt C. Ransom, executor, a case decided by the New
     York Court of Appeals on October 1, 1918, and reported at volume 120, page 639,
     of North Eastern Reporter.

     _____

     _____

10. Frank Floyd, et al. versus Billy Watson, et al., a case decided by the Supreme
     Court of Appeals in West Virginia on May 15, 1979, and reported at volume 254,
     page 687, of *South Eastern Reporter*, Second Series. You want to focus the
     reader's attention on material located on page 689.

     _____

     _____

Chapter 4

PARALLEL CITATIONS

Now that you have mastered the basic citation, you are ready to add a twist. The first thing we will add is the parallel citation. You learned from the previous exercises that some states have their opinions published in their own official reporter (referred to throughout this chapter as the state reporter) as well as the appropriate unofficial reporter published by West Group (referred to throughout this chapter as the regional reporter). For example, opinions from the Idaho Supreme Court and Idaho Court of Appeals are published in both *Idaho Reports* and *Pacific Reporter*. When you cite opinions from such a state to a court in that state, and when local rules of citation require it, Rule 12.4(c) calls for a citation to both the official and unofficial reporters. Remember also that some states have adopted public domain citation according to Rule 12.11 for citations to that state's opinions. When citing to decisions from those states to those states' courts, Rule 12.11 and many local rules require a public domain citation and a regional reporter citation.

The first decision you have to make is whether you need a parallel citation. If your case is from a federal court, you will not parallel cite. This rule extends to United States Supreme Court cases as well. Even though they are published in *United States Reports*, *Supreme Court Reporter*, and *Lawyers' Edition*, Rule 12.4(c) tells you to cite to only *United States Reports*.

A. STATES NOT REQUIRING PUBLIC DOMAIN CITATION

If your case is from a state that has its own reporter and you are citing this case in a document to a state court in that state, you will *usually* cite both the state and the regional reporters. The *ALWD Guide* directs you to first consult Appendix 2 for the local rules that tell whether a given state requires parallel citation. If local rules do require citation to more than one reporter, you will then use Appendix 1 in much the same way you do for any citation.

First, determine the jurisdiction of the case. Next, look up that jurisdiction in Appendix 1. Appendix 1 will tell you which reporters to cite and how those reporters are abbreviated. Rule 12.4(c) gives the appropriate order for listing reporters in a parallel citation. Usually, you will have only one official state reporter and the unofficial West regional reporter. In that case, list the state reporter first. If you have anything other than a state and regional reporter, consult 12.4(c) for the appropriate order of sources in the citation. Remember that some cases are printed in many different sources besides just state and regional reporters. Some publishers print subject matter reporters, compiling all the opinions in a certain subject area into one reporter. Also, some secondary research sources, such as *American Law Reports* (A.L.R.), publish the full text of opinions related to the articles they publish. Regardless of the number of publications in which your case is published, you will only cite to the reporters required by Appendix 2 and listed in Appendix 1.[1]

The next decision with a parallel citation is whether and how to identify the court that issued the opinion. Remember that the general rule, according to Rule 12.6(a), is that you do include the court abbreviation. Abbreviations for state courts can be found in each state's section of Appendix 1. Abbreviations for federal courts can be found in Appendix 4. However, 12.6(a) allows you to drop all or part of the court abbreviation if that part of the court abbreviation is obvious from one of the reporter abbreviations.

Lukowsky v. Shalit, 487 **N.Y.S.** 2d 781 (**App. Div.** 1985).

Remembering these rules might be easier if you know the rationale behind them. The basic rationale behind every citation rule is to keep the citation as short as possible while still conveying all significant information. This is why we generally include only the state and regional reporter and not every possible source that might publish an opinion. Likewise, why include the court abbreviation if it is obvious from the name of the reporter? Wait a minute . . . if brevity is so important, then why use a parallel citation at all? The answer is "convenience." Some practitioners and courts will subscribe only to the state reporter, usually because of financial or shelf-space constraints. A parallel citation helps people using only the state reporter from having to resort to a cross-reference index each time they want to look up a case.[2]

Let's try an example to see how these rules work. Suppose you are going to cite the Georgia Supreme Court case *Black v. Blue* in a brief you will file with the Georgia Court of Appeals. This is a 1972 case that is reported at volume 321, page 543, of *Georgia Reports*, Georgia's official state reporter. This opinion is also reported at volume 76, page 123, of *South Eastern Reporter*, Second Series. *South Eastern Reporter* is the unofficial West regional reporter that includes Georgia state cases.

Let's get the easy part of the citation out of the way first. We know we can start with the case name:

Black v. Blue,

Now, let's tackle the first decision: whether to include a parallel citation. This is a Georgia case, and we will be citing it to a Georgia court.

Remember that you want to first consult the local rules for the court the document will be submitted to in order to determine whether a parallel citation is required. Because we

---

[1] Do not be fooled by citations you read in reported cases! For example, opinions published in the West regional reporter system often contain parallel citations to other subject matter reporters published by West. These types of parallel citations do not conform to the *ALWD Guide* and should not be copied into your own writing.

[2] To accommodate lawyers and judges who need only a single state's case law, West publishes "offprints." You have probably noticed the reference in Appendix 1 to "West offprints." For example, in the Georgia section, after "South Eastern Reporter," you see a reference to "Georgia Cases (West offprint)." The West offprints are reporter volumes that include only the cases from a given state. For example, *South Eastern Reporter* contains cases from several states in addition to Georgia. However, practitioners in Georgia may only need the Georgia cases included in *South Eastern Reporter*. In that case, they can buy a version of *South Eastern Reporter* that contains only the cases from Georgia. This would be called the *Georgia Cases* (West offprint) of *South Eastern Reporter*. The citations in Georgia Cases are identical to those in *South Eastern Reporter*. Therefore, a parallel citation to both the regional reporter and the West offprint would be redundant and unnecessary.

will be citing this case to the Georgia Court of Appeals, we first go to the Georgia section of Appendix 2. In that section, we find that citations of Georgia cases to Georgia courts must include the volume and page number of the official Georgia reporter. This means that Georgia requires a parallel citation to the official state reporter as well as the standard citation to the unofficial regional reporter. Unless specifically instructed otherwise, you can assume that local rules requiring citation to the state reporter intend for you to cite the state reporter *in addition* to the regional reporter.

Although you will use Appendix 2 to determine which reporters to cite, you will consult Appendix 1 for the appropriate abbreviations for those reporters. Turning to the Georgia section of Appendix 1, we find that the official reporter is *Georgia Reports* and is abbreviated "Ga."; the unofficial reporter is *South Eastern Reporter*, and its Second Series is abbreviated "S.E.2d." So, those reporter abbreviations will be as follows:

321 Ga. 543

76 S.E.2d 123

Now that we have completed the first step, deciding which reporters to include and how to cite those reporters, we are ready for Step 2: determining in which order to place the reporters. For that, we will turn to Rule 12.4(c), which tells us that we should cite official reporters before unofficial reporters. Therefore, *Georgia Reports*, the official reporter, will be listed first. So, here we go!

Black v. Blue, 321 Ga. 543, 76 S.E.2d 123

Finally, Step 3 is deciding what to include for the court abbreviation in the court and date parenthetical. Turning to the Georgia section of Appendix 1, we find that the Georgia Supreme Court is abbreviated "Ga." Because "Ga." is also the abbreviation for the official reporter, the jurisdiction of the case will be obvious from the reporter abbreviation, and Rule 12.6(d) tells us that we do not have to repeat that information in the parenthetical. So, we will just add the year of the decision and a period, and we are done!

Black v. Blue, 321 Ga. 543, 76 S.E.2d 123 (1972).

Got it? Okay, now take a deep breath, and let's try the same citation in a court document filed with a federal court or a state court outside of Georgia that would not require a parallel cite for a Georgia case. In both of those cases, we only cite the unofficial West regional reporter. So the first thing we'll do is delete the citation to *Georgia Reports*.

Black v. Blue, 76 S.E.2d 123

Next, let's decide how to identify the court in the court and date parenthetical. Remember that Rule 12.6(a) requires a court abbreviation unless the name of the court is obvious from the reporter abbreviation. Because *South Eastern Reporter* publishes cases from many states, the reporter abbreviation is not sufficient to identify the court. Therefore, we must include the abbreviation for the Georgia Supreme Court—we found that abbreviation, "Ga.," earlier in Georgia's section of Appendix. 1.

Black v. Blue, 76 S.E.2d 123 (Ga.

Finish it off with the year of decision and a period at the end of our citation sentence, and we are done!

Black v. Blue, 76 S.E.2d 123 (Ga. 1972).

B. STATES REQUIRING PUBLIC DOMAIN CITATION

Remember from Chapter 2 that Appendix 2 tells which states require public domain citation. If a state does require public domain citation, Rule 12.11 and many local rules require a parallel citation including a public domain citation and a regional reporter citation. If you give a parallel citation that includes a public domain citation, Rule 12.11 does not require a court and date parenthetical. The reason for omitting the parenthetical is that the information that would ordinarily be in that parenthetical—state abbreviation, court abbreviation, and year of decision—is all included in the public domain citation. Therefore, a court and date parenthetical is unnecessary.

Let's run through an example of a parallel citation that includes public domain citation. Suppose we want to cite the Oklahoma Supreme Court case *Decorte v. Robinson*. This is a 1998 opinion that was issued as the 87th case by the court that year. The case is reported at volume 969, page 358 of *Pacific Reporter*, Second Series. *Pacific Reporter* is the regional reporter that includes Oklahoma state cases.

The first decision is whether our citation should include a public domain citation. To find this out, we check Oklahoma's section of Appendix 2 and find that Oklahoma has adopted the public domain citation format suggested by Rule 12.11. Therefore, we include both the public domain citation and a citation to the regional reporter. Let's start with the public domain citation. The first piece of information required is the year of decision.

> *Decorte v. Robinson*, 1998

Next, we add the public domain citation court abbreviation for the Oklahoma Supreme Court:

> *Decorte v. Robinson*, 1998 OK

Finally, we add the sequential number of the case that was assigned by the court.

> *Decorte v. Robinson*, 1998 OK 87

Now, let's add the citation for the regional reporter. We find the abbreviation for *Pacific Reporter*, Second Series (P.2d), in the Oklahoma section of Appendix 1. Because the reporter abbreviation contains only consecutive single capitals, Rule 2.2(a) tells us to close up all letters in the abbreviation.

> *Decorte v. Robinson*, 1998 OK 87, 969 P.2d 358

Because neither Rule 12.11 nor Oklahoma local rules require a court and date parenthetical with public domain citations, all we have to do is add a period to our citation sentence, and we're done!

Checklist for Parallel Citations

- Are you citing a state case?
    - If not, do not worry about parallel citation.
    - If so, are you citing the case to a state court in that same state?
        - If not, do not worry about parallel citation.
        - If so, turn to that state's section of Appendix 2 to determine whether that state has adopted public domain citation.
- If the state has **not** adopted public domain citation . . .
    - have you used Appendix 2 and Appendix 1 to determine which reporters to cite and how to abbreviate them?
    - have you listed state reporter(s) before the regional reporter?
    - have you placed the court and date parenthetical at the end of the citation as per Rule 12?
    - have you included a court abbreviation in the court and date parenthetical only if the name of the court is not obvious from the reporter abbreviation?
- If the state **has** adopted public domain citation . . .
    - have you listed the public domain citation first?
    - have you included the citation to the regional reporter if one is available?
    - have you omitted the court and date parenthetical?
- If the state has adopted a public domain citation format that differs from Rule 12.11, have you consulted local rules for the format and information to include?

Exercise 4
PARALLEL CITATIONS

Put the following information in correct *ALWD* citation form. All cases are being cited in citation sentences. Although this exercise builds on the rules used in previous exercises, this exercise focuses on Rules 12.4 and 12.6(c). You will also need to refer to Appendix 2 for information on which reporters to cite and Appendix 1 for reporter abbreviations. Do not include a public domain citation unless local rules in Appendix 2 require it.

1. In a brief filed with the Supreme Court of Oklahoma, you cite the 1912 Supreme Court of Appeals of West Virginia case Lyons versus Fairmont Real Estate Company. The case is reported in volume 71, page 754, of *West Virginia Reports* and in volume 77, page 525, of *South Eastern Reporter*.

_____

_____

2. In a brief to the Pennsylvania Supreme Court, you cite the 1950 Supreme Court of Oklahoma case West Edmond Salt Water Disposal Association versus L.T. Rosecrans, et al. This case is reported in volume 204, page 9, of *Oklahoma Reports* and in volume 226, page 965, of *Pacific Reporter,* Second Series. Pennsylvania Rule of Appellate Procedure 126 states that parties may cite to the National Reporter System alone.

_____

_____

3. In a brief to the Fourteenth District Court of Appeals in Texas, you cite the 1983 Supreme Court of Texas case Earl Gooden, et al., Appellants, versus Eugene Tips, M.D., Appellee. The case is reported in volume 651, page 364, of *South Western Reporter*, Second Series, and in volume 43, page 139, of *American Law Reports*, Fourth Series. The State of Texas ceased publication of its state reporter in 1962.

_____

_____

4. In a brief to the Supreme Court of Arkansas, you cite the September 23, 1985, Supreme Court of Arkansas case Grain Dealers Mutual Insurance Company, Appellant versus Helen Porterfield, Appellee. This case is reported in volume 287, page 27, of *Arkansas Reports;* in volume 695, page 833, of *South Western Reporter*, Second Series; and in volume 27, page 977, of *Education Law Reports*. It is the practice of Arkansas courts to cite to both the official and national reporter for Arkansas cases.

_____

_____

5. In a brief to the Supreme Court of Oregon, you cite the 1985 Supreme Court of Washington case Larry Daugert, Trustee for David M. Simms & Gail Simms versus John D. Pappas & Betty Pappas. This case is reported in volume 104, page 254, of *Washington Reports*, Second Series, and in volume 704, page 600, of *Pacific Reporter*, Second Series.

---

6. In a brief filed with the Iowa Supreme Court, you cite the 1965 Supreme Court of Mississippi case Carl Murphy, Jr. versus Joshua Allen Randolph Beckett. The case is reported in volume 253, page 644, of *Mississippi Reports*, and in volume 178, page 692, of *Southern Reporter*, Second Series.

---

7. In a brief to the United States Supreme Court, you cite the 1985 Court of Appeals of Maryland case Olen J. Kelley, et ux. versus R.G. Industries, Inc., et al. This case is reported in volume 54, page 2195, of *United States Law Week*; in volume 44, page 563, of *American Law Reports*, Fourth Series; in volume 497, page 1143, of *Atlantic Reporter*, Second Series; and in volume 304, page 124, of *Maryland Reports*. It is the practice of the United States Supreme Court to cite to the national reporter system for state cases.

---

8. In a brief filed with the Nebraska Supreme Court, you cite the 1999 Supreme Court of Nebraska case Ann Kennedy Elsome, appellee, versus Paul T. Elsome, appellant. The case is reported in volume 257, page 889, of *Nebraska Reports*, and in volume 601, page 537, of *North Western Reporter*, Second Series.

---

9. In a brief filed with the South Dakota Supreme Court, you cite the 2008 South Dakota Supreme Court case Lorraine Kirksey versus Dorothy E. Grohmann. This case is reported in volume 754, page 825, of *North Western Reporter*, Second Series. This case was given the sequential number of 76 by the South Dakota Supreme Court. (Note: South Dakota has changed its public domain citation rules since the printed edition of the guide – see court website for format).

---

10. In a brief filed with the Montana Supreme Court, you cite the 2008 Montana Supreme Court case Rodney Barnard, Petitioner, versus Liberty Northwest Insurance Corporation, respondent. This case is reported in volume 189, page 1196, of *Pacific Reporter*, Third Series, and in volume 345 of *Montana Reports* beginning on page 81. It was given the sequential number of 254 by the Montana Supreme Court.

Chapter 5

SHORT FORMS (CASES)

Frequently, you will wish to refer to one case several times within a legal memorandum or a court document. Just to prove to you that the *ALWD Guide* does indeed have a heart, you need only give the full legal citation for a case the *first* time you cite to that case. Citing a case in full after having mentioned the case before will, in fact, confuse your reader. Your reader may think you are introducing a new case into your analysis. For all subsequent cites to that case, you will use a short form citation, as long as all subsequent cites are within the same general discussion. Rules 11.2, 11.3, and 12.16 provide information on short form citations for cases. You should read each of those sections carefully before attempting Exercise 5.

The *ALWD Guide* provides two types of short forms to be used for cases in legal memoranda and court documents: "*id.*" and an abbreviated version of the full legal citation. These two types are not interchangeable, but can each be used only in certain instances. (Note that "*supra*" may also be used as a permissible short form for some types of sources. However, according to Rule 11.4(b), "*supra*" is not a permissible short form for cases or statutes.)

Rule 11.3 explains the short form "*id.*" in detail and gives good examples.[1] The short form "*id.*" may be used only when you wish to cite to a case that is cited in the *immediately preceding citation*. In other words, no intervening cites to a different authority of any type should appear between the preceding citation to this case and the current citation. However, the preceding citation to the case may be a full citation or a short form citation, even another "*id.*" designation. Note, however, that simply mentioning a case name in a previous sentence will not support an "*id.*" citation. In addition, the prior citation need only be to the same case, not to the same page in the same case. If you wish to cite to the same page of the same case, then use only the word "*id.*" If you wish to cite to a different page or pages of the same case, use the word *id.* but also those page numbers immediately preceded by the word "at."

> Prior to being arrested, Mrs. Jones had accumulated over 100 speeding tickets. *State v. Jones*, 16 Rptr. 33, 34 (St. Ct. 1999). The majority of these tickets listed her speed as at least 20 miles per hour over the posted speed limit. *Id.* Five of the speeding tickets were issued in connection with traffic accidents. *Id.* at 35.

Two more details to remember: If the immediately preceding citation is a "string cite," *i.e.*, contains more than one authority, then you may not use "*id.*," even if one of those

---

[1] "Id." is an abbreviation for "idem," a latin word meaning "the same." It is not capitalized unless it begins a citation sentence. The period following the abbreviation is italicized, as provided in Rule 11.3(b). In your earlier studies prior to law school, you may have used "Ibid.," which is an abbreviation for the Latin word "ibidem," which means "the same place." For whatever reason, legal writing has developed using only "id."

authorities is the case you currently wish to cite. Consider the following three cites that appear consecutively in a paragraph.

State v. Jones, 16 Rptr. 33, 34 (St. Ct. 1999).

Id.; *State v. Smith*, 19 Rptr. 389, 390–392 (St. Ct. 2002).

Smith, 19 Rptr. at 390–92.

The second citation is a string cite referring to both *Jones* and *Smith*. Because *Jones* was the immediately preceding citation, "*id.*" clearly refers to that case. "*Id.*" may be the first part of a string cite. However, notice that the third citation, a reference to *Smith*, is not "*id.*" even though *Smith* is part of the immediately preceding citation. This is because "*id.*" cannot be used to refer to a single source within a string cite. When you think about it, this makes sense. If the second citation above were followed by "*id.*" the reader would likely think you intended a citation to both of the sources in the string cite.

When circumstances do not allow you to use "*id.*," Rule 12.16(b) and (c) provide for the use of an abbreviated short form to refer to previous citations to cases. The *ALWD Guide* provides a very practical system for constructing short forms for cases. According to Rule 12.16(c), if you have referred to the case by name in your textual sentence, the short form to use in your citation sentence will consist only of the volume number, the reporter abbreviation, and the page number, preceded by the word "at." You drop the court and date parenthetical completely. Therefore, the short form for *Tortoise v. Hare*, 467 N.2d 1 (Ct. 2000), in that situation would be as follows:

In the case mentioned previously, *Tortoise v. Hare*, the plaintiff sued on the theory of breach of an implied contract. 467 N.2d at 3.

If, however, you have not referred to the case by name in that specific textual sentence, then the appropriate short form to use, according to Rule 12.16(b), will retain one party's name.

In the case mentioned previously, *Tortoise v. Hare*, the plaintiff sued on the theory of breach of an implied contract. 467 N.2d at 3. The facts in this case are similar to the facts of a more recent case, in which the plaintiff also alleged an implied contract. *Androcles v. Lion*, 352 N.2d 54 (St. App. 2007). In both cases, the plaintiff prevailed at trial. *Id.* at 59; *Tortoise*, 467 N.2d at 7.

Rule 12.16(b) strongly suggests retaining the first party's name instead of the second party's name unless such use will be confusing. For example, you would not choose the name of a party that is frequently named in litigation, such as a state, the United States, a governmental agency, or the head of an agency or branch of government of either a state or the United States. In addition, Rule 12.16(b) suggests shortening a party's name if the name is long. Therefore, for the case *State v. Roach*, 772 A.2d 395 (N.J. 2001), you would choose as your short form.

Roach, 772 A.2d at 400.

NOT:

State, 772 A.2d at 400.

If the full citation of your case is a parallel citation with two or more reporter references, then craft your abbreviated short form in accordance with Rule 12.16(d). Again, you would drop the first page on which your case appears in each reporter and the court and date parenthetical, but include the relevant page information for each reporter preceded by the word "at."

Roach, 167 N.J. at 600, 772 A.2d at 400.

For the use of "*id.*" with a parallel citation, Rule 12.16(d) allows you to substitute "*id.*" for the official state reporter information in the first part of your citation.

Id. at 600, 772 A.2d at 400.

Checklist for Case Short Forms

- Did you cite to the current case in the immediately preceding citation? If so, use "*id.*" If not, then you cannot use "*id.*" and must use an abbreviated short form.

- Does the immediately preceding citation contain more than one authority, *i.e.*, is it a string cite? If so, then you cannot use "*id.*" and must use an abbreviated short form.

- If you cannot use "*id.*," have you formulated an acceptable abbreviated short form?

- In your abbreviated short form, have you retained the volume and reporter name from the full legal citation?

- If the full citation contained a parallel citation, have you included references to both reporters in the short form?

- In your abbreviated short form, have you used the word "at" and a pinpoint page number?

Exercise 5
SHORT FORMS (CASES)

Put the following information in correct *ALWD* citation form. All cases are being cited in citation sentences in text, not footnotes. Although this exercise builds on the rules used in previous exercises, this exercise focuses on Rules 11 and 12.16. In composing the short forms of party names, be guided by the information in each problem and assume that no part of the case name has been included in the textual sentence preceding unless specifically told that information.

1. In the immediately preceding sentence of a legal memorandum, without an intervening cite, you cited to *Mitsubishi Motors Corp. v. Soler Chrysler-Plymouth*, Inc., 473 U.S. 614 (1985). You now wish to cite to page 616 of the case.

2. Two paragraphs later in the same document, after citing to other cases and a statute, you wish to cite to page 616 of *Mitsubishi Motors Corp. v. Soler Chrysler-Plymouth, Inc.*, 473 U.S. 614 (1985), again. You have referred to this case in your textual sentence as "*Mitsubishi Motors.*"

3. On page 3 of your legal memorandum, you cited to *Nat'l Iranian Oil v. Ashland Oil, Inc.*, 817 F.2d 326 (5th Cir. 1987). On page 6, you would like to cite to *Nat'l Iranian Oil* again, only you would like to focus your reader's attention on information beginning on page 328 and continuing on page 329. You have cited to other cases on pages 4 and 5 of your memorandum. You have not referred to the case by name in your textual sentence, but elsewhere you have referred to the case as "*Nat'l Iranian Oil.*"

4. In the next sentence, you would like to cite to the same information again. No intervening cites appear between the citation in #3 and the current cite.

5. In the same legal memorandum, you again wish to refer to *Mitsubishi Motors Corp. v. Soler Chrysler-Plymouth, Inc.*, 473 U.S. 614 (1985), focusing your reader's attention on information on page 617. The immediately preceding citation sentence reads "*Mitsubishi Motors*, 473 U.S. at 617; *Natl. Iranian Oil Co. v. Ashland Oil, Inc.*, 817 F.2d 326 (5th Cir. 1987)." Draft the appropriate short form. You have not referred to the case by name in your textual sentence, but elsewhere you have referred to the case as "*Mitsubishi Motors.*"

6. In a brief to a New York court, you have previously cited to *Mobil Oil Indon. Inc. v. Asamera (Indon.) Ltd.*, 56 A.D.2d 339, 392 N.Y.S.2d 614 (1977). You wish to cite to *Mobil Oil* again after several intervening cites, focusing your reader on information contained at 56 A.D.2d 341 and 392 N.Y.S.2d 616, respectively. You have not referred to the case by name in your textual sentence, but when you have done so, you have referred to it as "*Mobil Oil*."

7. In the next sentence, without any intervening cites, you would like to cite to *Mobil Oil* again, only this time you would like to direct your reader's attention to information found at 56 A.D.2d 342 and 392 N.Y.S.2d 617. You have not referred to the case by name in your textual sentence.

8. On page 68 of a brief to the Fifth Circuit Court of Appeals, you cite to *United States v. Lipshy*, 492 F. Supp. 35 (N.D. Tex. 1979). On page 82 of your brief, you would like to refer to this case again, focusing your reader's attention on information beginning on page 37 and continuing on page 38. You have cited to other cases in the interim. You have not referred to the case by name in your textual sentence.

9. You wish to formulate a short form, not "*id.*," for information found on the first page of *Katzenbach v. McClung*, 379 U.S. 294 (1964). You have not referred to the case by name in the textual sentence. [*Hint: Nicholas Katzenbach was the acting Attorney General of the United States and was named in many civil rights cases during that time.*]

10. You wish to formulate a short form, not "*id.*," for information found on page 428 and continuing on page 429 of *Bunge v. First Nat'l Bank of Mount Holly Springs, P.A.*, 118 F.2d 427 (3d Cir. 1941). You have not referred to the case by name in your textual sentence.

Chapter 6

FEDERAL STATUTES

The general rules for citing federal statutes are located in Chapter 14 of the *ALWD Guide*. The rules relating to rules of procedure and rules of evidence, which are codified with the federal statutes, appear in a separate chapter, Chapter 16. Citation of the United States Constitution is the subject of Chapter 13. You will also need to be familiar with Rule 6 for section symbols and spacing.

Both the federal statutes and the United States Constitution are published in an official compilation, the *United States Code*. Although technically not statutes, the federal rules of procedure and evidence are also published in the *United States Code*. The *United States Code* is divided into subject matter areas called "titles." Each title is numbered and may span more than one hard-bound volume. Within each title, each statute is given a section number and may be divided into subsections. If possible, always cite the *United States Code*, which is the official code. Otherwise, you may cite to the *United States Code Annotated* or the *United States Code Service*.

To get a start on federal statutory citation form, look at the citations analyzed in Rule 14.2 of the *ALWD Guide*. The basic "formula" for a federal statute citation follows:

Title U.S.C. § Section (Date).

Rule 14.2(a) tells us that we may include the name of the act, but the name is not mandatory. If included, the name of the act appears in ordinary type at the beginning of the statute, similar to the name of a case.

Clean Water Act, 33 U.S.C. § 1314(a)(1) (2012).

The first required component of the citation is the title number, which is analogous to a case citation's volume number. In a federal statutory citation, the title number precedes the name of the code cited just as the volume number of a case reporter precedes the name of the reporter in a case citation. The section number follows the abbreviated code just as the page number follows the abbreviated reporter name in a case citation:

123 U.S. 456

28 U.S.C. § 1291

You cite individual code sections by using a single section symbol (§) followed by the section number. Rule 6.2 tells you to insert a space between the section symbol and the section number. To indicate that you are citing to more than one numbered section, use a double section symbol (§§) followed by a space and the section numbers. Rule 6.3(a) tells you to indicate a span of consecutive sections or subsections by using a hyphen between the inclusive numbers. To cite to nonconsecutive sections or subsections, use a comma and a space to separate the section numbers.

28 U.S.C. §§ 1331-1367, 1441-1452 (2012).

28 U.S.C. §§ 1331, 1441 (2012).

Note, however, that you do not use double section symbols when you are citing to multiple subsections within the same numbered section.

28 U.S.C. § 1367(a)-(b) (2012).

When citing multiple subsubsections of a statute, you will generally follow the same rules as those for citing sections. When dealing with subsubsections, you will not repeat digits or letters.

28 U.S.C. § 105(b)(1), (5)

19 U.S.C. § 1490(a)(1)(A)-(C)

NOT:

28 U.S.C. § 105(b)(1), (b)(5)

19 U.S.C. § 1490(a)(1)(A)-(a)(1)(C)

Look again at the full citations given above. The last element in each is a year in parentheses. Rule 14.2(f) governs the insertion of the date in your citation. The U.S.C. main volumes are published every six years. The code is kept up to date between complete publications by annual supplements. When you are researching and citing federal statutes, you must make sure that the statutory provisions you are using and citing are the ones currently in effect.

If all of your cited material appears in the main volume, then you simply include the year the main volume was published. If all of your cited material appears in a supplement, then you indicate this by including the abbreviation "Supp." and the year the supplement was published. If your reader would need to consult both the main volume and a supplement, then you must include both pieces of information, connected by an ampersand (&).

Title U.S.C. § Section (Year & Supp. Year).

Let's walk through a federal statutory citation to get you started. Let's put section 501 of title 17 of the *United States Code* into a citation sentence. Subsection (a) of the statute is in the 2013 Supplement, but all remaining provisions are in the main volume, published in 2012. We are not using the name of the act of which this statute is a part, so you know from Rule 14.2(a) that the first element of a federal statutory citation is the number of the title. In our statute that number is 17. Next is the abbreviation of the code. Following the information on federal courts, Appendix 1 shows the proper abbreviations and formats for "Statutory compilations." You see that the abbreviation for the *United States Code* is "U.S.C." Rule 2.2(a) tells you to close up adjacent single capitals, so make sure there are no spaces in "U.S.C."

17 U.S.C.

Next comes a section symbol followed by a space. After the section symbol and space, you will insert the section number. In this example, assume that also wish to cite to a subsection, (c). Rule 6.2 tells you to use the original punctuation (meaning the punctuation used in the code itself) dividing sections from subsections. Therefore, our complete statute number is 501(c). Note that no spaces are inserted between the main section and the subsection.

17 U.S.C. § 501(c)

The final element is the year. You already know that the statute is currently in force and that you are citing the official code. Therefore, according to Rule 14.2(f), you do not have to show the name of a publisher. You know also that the main volumes of the current official code were published in 2012, and the supplement was published in 2013.

17 U.S.C. § 501(c) (2012 & Supp. 2013).

In addition to these rules for citing most statutes, you do need to know some rules for some specific statutes. For example, Appendix 6 governs citation to federal taxation materials, including the Internal Revenue Code, which is located in Title 26 of the *United States Code*. Appendix 6 tells you that when citing to the Internal Revenue Code, you may cite to "I.R.C." rather than to title 26 of the *United States Code*.

I.R.C. § 703(a) (2012).

NOT:

26 U.S.C. § 703(a) (2012).

In addition, Rule 16.1 tells us that cites to the current version of certain rules, such as the Federal Rules of Civil Procedure, which are published in an appendix to the *United States Code*, do not cite to the *United States Code*, but instead cite only to the rules themselves. A citation to the current version of the rule does not require a date parenthetical.

Fed. R. Civ. P. 26(b)(4).

A cite to a statute or constitutional provision that you have found on an electronic database is identical to the citation to the printed code except in the date parenthetical. When citing a statute available on an electronic database, include the following information:

- the regular statute citation and
- in the parenthetical, the current publisher's name, the name of the database, and the date through which the statute is current, as stated by the database itself.

Statute Citation (Publisher, Database current through Month Day, Year).

42 U.S.C.A. § 1751 (West, WestlawNext current through Pub. L. No. 113-13, approved June 3, 2013).

42 U.S.C.S. § 1751 (LexisNexis, Lexis Advance current through Pub. L. No. 113-22, approved July 25, 2013).

Checklist for Federal Statutes

- If you are using the name of the statute, have you put that name first in ordinary type?
- Have you put the title number before the name of the code?
- Have you properly abbreviated the name of the code?
- Have you closed up (left no spaces between) all adjacent single capitals in the abbreviated name of the code?
- Have you inserted a single section symbol for a single statute and a double section symbol for more than one statute?
- Have you left a single space between the section symbol and the section number?
- Have you closed up the section number and its subsections?
- Have you put the year(s) of publication in parentheses at the end of your citation?
- If any portion of your cited material is included in a supplementary volume, have you indicated this in the date parenthetical?
- Have you left a space between the last character of the section number and the date parenthetical?
- Have you ended your citation sentence with a period?

Exercise 6
FEDERAL STATUTES

Put the following information in correct *ALWD* citation form. All statutes are being cited in citation sentences. This exercise focuses on Rules 13.1 through 14.2(f), and Rules 16.1 through 16.1(c).

1. The Eleventh Amendment to the Constitution of the United States.

    _____

    _____

2. Section 1101(1) of title 11 of the current *United States Code*, published in 2018. This section appears in its entirety in the 2018 main volume.

    _____

    _____

3. Subsection (a)(6) of section 523 of title 11 of the current *United States Code*, published in 2018. This section appears in its entirety in the 2018 main volume.

    _____

    _____

4. Subsections (a) through (b) of Section 764 of title 15 of the current *United States Code*, published in 2012. This section appears in its entirety in the 2012 main volume.

    _____

    _____

5. Subsections (b) and (d) of Section 4304 of title 41 of the current *United States Code*. Part of this citation appears in the 2012 main volume, and part appears in the 2017 Supplement V.

    _____

    _____

6. Rule 56(e) of the current Federal Rules of Civil Procedure, published in the Appendix to title 28 of the *United States Code* in the 2012 bound volume.

    _____

    _____

7. Rule 801(d) of the current Federal Rules of Evidence, published in the Appendix to title 28 of the *United States Code* in the 2017 Supplement V.

    _____

    _____

8. Section 231v(a) through (c) of title 45 of the current *United States Code*. These subsections appear in their entirety in the 2015 Supplement III.

_____

_____

9. In a discussion of the current version of certain federal tax law provisions, cite section 2036(a) of the *Internal Revenue Code*, title 26 of the current *United States Code*, published in 2012. Use the special citation form for tax law provisions.

_____

_____

10. Section 1332(a)(2) and (a)(4) of title 28 of the current *United States Code*, which was printed in the main volume published in 2012.

_____

_____

Chapter 7

STATE STATUTES

Rule 14.4 generally governs state statute citations. The rule, however, basically serves to refer you to each state's listing in Appendix 1. Please read Rule 14.4 and glance through your state's listing in Appendix 1.

The citation form for federal statutes and state statutes is similar; however, the challenge here is that each state has a different system of compiling and publishing statutes. Thus, each state has a slightly different citation form for statutes. Generally, each citation will include the following:

- an abbreviated name of the state code;
- possibly the name of a subject matter if the code is arranged by subject matter;
- numerical information pointing the reader to a specific statutory provision;
- possibly the publisher of the code; and
- the year of publication.

In each state's entry in Appendix 1, you will find a template for what information to include and in what form. This listing also includes the proper abbreviation for each state code. Therefore, for each state statute that you cite, you should always refer to that state's page in Appendix 1 for a fool-proof "formula." You may also need to consult Rule 2.2 to ensure that you are spacing the abbreviation correctly.

Most statutes are not organized by pages as cases are. Instead, most statutes are arranged by sections, but may also be arranged by chapters, titles, paragraphs, subdivisions, or a combination thereof. Therefore, in addition to consulting Appendix 1, you will also need to pay attention to Rule 6.1 with regard to sections and paragraphs. Broadly, remember that you indicate that you are citing to multiple sections by using two section symbols without a space in between. Note, however, that you need a space between the section symbol and the actual section number.

Ariz. Rev. Stat. Ann. §§ 17-454, 17-456 (2006).

Del. Code Ann. tit. 3, § 10105(a) (2001).

Alaska Stat. § 37.14.400 (2006).

The only other detail you need to know to master the basics of state statute citation is how to determine the date of the code. Note that the year of the code is NOT the date the particular statute was enacted. To avoid this confusion, remember the purpose of the date in the citation: to help your reader know how to find a particular statute. To do this, your reader must know what version of a code to consult, *i.e.*, the version of the code published in a particular year. In addition, your reader must know whether the information is contained in the main body of the code, a supplement or pocket part, or both. Therefore, you need to include this information. Rule 8.2 tells us to glean the date of the code for date parenthetical purposes from the date on the copyright page. If the entirety of the section that you are citing appears in the main volume, use only the date for the main volume.

Del. Code Ann. tit. 7, § 931 (2001).

Often, part or all of the section will have been amended and reprinted in a supplementary volume that is either bound separately from the main volume or attached in a pocket located in the inside back cover of the main volume. Rule 8.3 gives insight into citing material that appears in both the main volume and the supplement.

Del. Code Ann. tit. 7, § 927 (2001 & Supp. 2006).

Many times, a newly enacted statute will appear only in the supplement or pocket part. In these cases, you should include only the year of the supplement pursuant to Rule 8.1.

Del. Code Ann. tit. 7, § 517(c) (Supp. 2006).

Finally, some states, such as California and Michigan, have more than one statutory compilation. Generally, the *ALWD Guide* prefers citations to the official state code, if possible. Appendix 1 indicates which compilation to cite, if available, by noting each official code with a star (☆).

Like federal statutes, state statutes may also be cited electronically. If you do not have access to the print version of the code you are citing, you may cite to the electronic version. This is increasingly common with statutes. Unlike court opinions, statutes do not have a fixed, permanent year. A given statute may be amended or supplemented through the years. Therefore, the year is a piece of information that has to be updated each time the statute is cited. If you access statutes through only electronic databases, you will also not have access to the current information about the year of the print statute. In that case, you would cite to the electronic version of the statute.

Citation to the electronic source differs only in the parenthetical. Rather than indicating the year of the main volume and/or supplement, you will give the date information provided by the electronic database. In an electronic database, statutes are updated on a rolling basis without set publication dates of volumes and pocket parts. Electronic databases tell you how current the statute is that you are reading on your computer screen with language such as "current through the 2015 Special Session." You add this information, plus the name of the database, to the date parenthetical. Neither the ALWD Guide nor the Bluebook tell you to abbreviate the information. However, the examples in both manuals include abbreviations. Therefore, the correct ICW answer will also include abbreviations based on this formula: Abbreviate any words found in Appendix 3 and drop any articles ("a," "an," "the").

Wash. Rev. Code Ann. § 9.41.280(1)(a) (Westlaw through 2015 Spec. Sess.).

Because statutes are not assigned a unique database identifier, the short form for a statute found on an electronic database will look very similar to a short form for a statute found in a bound volume.

§ 9.41.280(1)(a).

Checklist for State Statutes

- Have you consulted Appendix 1 for the correct abbreviation of the state code?
- Have you followed the format for the state statute given in Appendix 1?
- Have you taken the year of the code from the copyright information in the appropriate volume?
- Does all of the information cited appear in the main volume?
    - If so, then include only the year of the main volume in the parenthetical.
    - If a portion of the statute cited is in a supplement, then include the date of the main volume and the supplement.
- Does all of the information cited appear in a supplement? If so, then include the date of only the supplement.

Exercise 7
STATE STATUTES

Put the following information in correct *ALWD* citation form. All statutes are being cited in citation sentences. Although this exercise builds on the rules used in previous exercises and generally follows Rule 14.2 for federal statutes, this exercise focuses on state rather than federal statutes. You will need to refer to Rules 13 and 14.4 and Appendix 1 for information on the statutes in the appropriate jurisdiction. If an online code is authenticated or official, cite the date of the publication as you would the bound volume rather than a commercial database.

1. Section 291-52 of Michie's *Hawaii Revised Statutes Annotated*, all of which appears in the 2018 bound volume.

   _____

   _____

2. Sections 213.1087 and 213.1099 of *Nevada Revised Statutes*, all of which appear in the 2019 main volume.

   _____

   _____

3. Section 16-11-129 of the official version of the *Official Code of Georgia Annotated*. The copyright date is 2018. However, part of the section appears in the 2019 pocket part.

   _____

   _____

4. Section 18.2-387 of the *Code of Virginia 1950 Annotated*, which is published by LexisNexis. The copyright date is 2014. No amendments to this section appear in any supplement or pocket part.

   _____

   _____

5. Section 41.181(4)(a) of the *Michigan Compiled Laws Annotated*, published by West. You do not have the Michigan code available to you in print. However, you do have a subscription to Westlaw, which has that code available. The database states that it is current "through P.A.2019, No. 178, of the 2019 Regular Session, 100th Legislature."

   _____

   _____

6. Section 45-2-102(A) of Michie's *Annotated Statutes of New Mexico*, published by LexisNexis. You do not have the New Mexico code available to you in print. However, you do have a subscription to Lexis Advance, which has that code available. The database states that it is current "through all legislation for the 2019 Regular Session."

_____

_____

7. Section 31-231 of the *Arizona Revised Statutes Annotated*. You do not have the official code available to you in print. However, you do have a subscription to Westlaw, which has the official code available. The database states that it is current "through the First Regular Session of the Fifty-Fourth Legislature (2019)."

_____

_____

8. Section 1632(a) through (c) of West's *Annotated California Civil Code*. The statute appears in the 2011 bound volume, but it has been amended and reprinted in its entirety in the 2020 supplement.

_____

_____

9. Section 60K of chapter 231 of the *Massachusetts General Laws Annotated*, published by West. The copyright date on the volume in which this statute appears is 2018.

_____

_____

10. Section 24-2-201 of the *Arkansas Code of 1987 Annotated*, published by LexisNexis. This section appears in its entirety in the 2014 main volume.

_____

_____

11. Section 35.01 of the *Arts & Cultural Affairs Laws of New York Annotated*, which is published in a volume of McKinney's *Consolidated Laws of New York Annotated*. This entire section appears in the 2017 main volume.

_____

_____

12. Title 17, section 2518 of the *Maine Revised Statutes Annotated*. The entire relevant section appears in the 2018 pocket part.

_____

_____

13. Title 54, section 355(D) of the *Oklahoma Statutes 2011*. It is the official reporter that is currently published under direction from the Oklahoma Supreme Court by the West company. (West also publishes the commercial version *Oklahoma Statutes Annotated*.) The copyright date of this volume is 2011. This section does not appear in any supplement or pocket part.

---

14. Title 6, section 18-108 of the *Delaware Code Annotated*. The copyright date is 2013. However, you accessed this particular statute through the State of Delaware's authenticated code online, which is found at http://delcode.delaware.gov. This section does not appear in any supplement or pocket part.

---

15. Subsections 36-4-2(a)(1) through (4) of the *General Laws of Rhode Island*. These sections appear in their entirety in the 2019 pocket part. Assume that using a hyphen to indicate the span of subsections would be ambiguous.

Chapter 8

SHORT FORMS (STATUTES)

As with cases, you will often refer to a statute several times within a legal memorandum or a court document. Similarly, the *ALWD Guide* states that you need to give the full legal citation for a statute only the *first* time that you cite to that statute. Thereafter, you will use a short form citation to that statute. Rules 14.5 and 11 provide information on short form citations for state and federal statutes. Rule 13.4 gives us guidance as to short form citations for state and federal constitutions. You should read each of those sections carefully before attempting Exercise 8.

As with cases, the *ALWD Guide* provides two types of short forms to be used for statutes in legal memoranda and court documents: "*id.*" and an abbreviated version of the full legal citation. The rules for when you may use each type parallel the rules that we discussed in connection with cases. You may use the short form "*id.*" only when you are citing to a statute previously cited in the immediately preceding citation (and only if that previous citation is not a string cite). Again, no intervening cites to a different authority of any type should appear between the previous cite to this statute and the current citation.

You learned in Exercise 5 (Short Forms (Cases)) that you use "*id.*" to refer to a previous case even when you want to cite to a different page. Similarly, the previous citation to a statute need not be to the exact section or subsection of your statute; however, you will need to include any information in your citation that differs from the immediately preceding citation. The proper formulation is simply the word "*id.*" followed by the new section or subsection information.

Because Rule 11.3(d) tells you that you should indicate in an "*id.*" cite only the way in which that citation differs from the previous one, you will omit the code abbreviation and the date and publisher parenthetical, provided that the material is the same for the "*id.*" cite as for the original citation. However, you should reproduce the entire section number for clarity if only the subsection changes. Although this rule is not stated expressly, it can be inferred from the examples following Rule 11.3(d). Notice in the example below that the second citation includes both the section and subsection information rather than just the different subsection. Notice that the third citation includes also the date parenthetical because section 1-201(b)(2) is in the 2010 Supplement, but the original section cited was in the 2007 main volume. Notice also that while citations here are in bold type to emphasize them for you, they should not be in bold type in the normal course of writing.

In our jurisdiction, "fruit" is defined as an edible part of a plant that contains seeds. **St. Stat. Ann. § 1-201(a) (2007).** A "vegetable" is defined as an edible part of a plant that does not contain seeds. ***Id.* § 1-201(b)(1).** However, the term "vegetable" does not include legumes or tubers. ***Id.*** Recently, the legislature determined that a cucumber, although it contains seeds, would be deemed to be a vegetable. *Id.* § 1-201(b)(4) **(Supp. 2010)**.

In those circumstances when you wish to use a short form but cannot use "*id.*," you will use an abbreviated form of the full citation. Rule 14.5 gives you several abbreviation options. You may omit just the date parenthetical, omit the title of the publication and the date parenthetical, or omit the title of the publication, any chapter or title number, and the date parenthetical. This concept is easier to convey in examples:

36 U.S.C. § 301 (2012).

becomes:

36 U.S.C. § 301.

or

§ 301.

Md. Fin. Inst. Code Ann. § 13-708.1 (2003).

becomes:

Md. Fin. Inst. Code Ann. § 13-708.1.

or

§ 13-708.1

Vt. Stat. Ann. tit. 13 § 2405 (2002).

becomes:

Vt. Stat. Ann. tit. 13 § 2405

or

tit. 13 § 2405.

or

§ 2405.

You will eventually develop your own preferences, but your ultimate objective should be clarity for your reader. For purposes of the ICW exercises, assume a preference for the first listed short form or an "*id.*" form, whichever is appropriate.

Checklist for Statutory Short Forms

- Did you cite to the current statute in the immediately preceding citation? If not, then you cannot use *"id."*

- Does the immediately preceding citation contain more than one authority, *i.e.*, is it a string cite? If so, then you cannot use *"id."*

- If you cannot use *"id.,"* have you formulated an acceptable abbreviated short form?

Exercise 8
SHORT FORMS (STATUTES)

Put the following information in correct *ALWD* citation form. All statutes are being cited in citation sentences. Although this exercise builds on the rules used in previous exercises, this exercise focuses on Rules 11.2, 11.3, and 14.5. You will need to refer to Appendix 1 for information on the statutes in the appropriate jurisdiction.

1. In the immediately preceding sentence of a legal memorandum, you cited to a provision in the *West's Annotated California Codes*, Cal. Civ. Code § 1543 (West Supp. 2020). Without an intervening cite, you wish to cite to this same statute.

_____

_____

2. On the next page of your memorandum, after citing to several other authorities, you wish to cite again to Cal. Civ. Code § 1543 (West Supp. 2020). In your memo, you have cited to statutes from other states and to provisions in other California subject matter codes. You are concerned that your reader may be confused, so you want your short form to be clear.

_____

_____

3. In the very next sentence of your memorandum, without an intervening cite, you wish to cite to another provision of the *California Civil Code*, Cal. Civ. Code § 1549 (West Supp. 2020).

_____

_____

4. Earlier in the same general discussion, you cited to Idaho Code § 29-102 (2018). Now, two pages later, you wish to cite to section 29-101. Several cites to other authorities appear on the two intervening pages. You have not cited to any other statutes in this memo and think the shortest abbreviation will be best because there is no risk of confusion to the reader.

_____

_____

5. On page 3 of a different memorandum, you cited to a provision of the *Code of Virginia 1950 Annotated*, Va. Code Ann. § 8.2-716(1) (2015). In the next line, you again cite to the same provision, using the short form "*id.*" In the next paragraph, without any intervening cites, you wish to cite to subsection (2) of the same provision.

_____

_____

6. In the same paragraph, without any intervening cites, you again wish to cite to subsection (2) of Va. Code Ann. § 8.2-716.

   _____

7. In an appellate brief, you wish to cite to section 5342(b) of the *California Corporations Code*, which is a part of *West's Annotated California Codes*. The immediately preceding cite reads "Cal. Corp. Code § 5342(b) (West 2014); Cal. Civ. Code § 1559 (West 1982)." Because you are citing to several California codes, you are concerned with the risk of confusion to your reader.

   _____

8. In a legal memorandum, you have previously cited to a New York statute, N.Y. Crim. Proc. Law § 700.05(1)–(2) (McKinney 2009). Three paragraphs later, with several intervening cites to different authorities, you wish to cite to the same two subsections. Because you are citing to several New York subject matter codes, you are concerned that your reader will be confused unless you identify each statute with particularity.

   _____

9. In the next sentence, without any intervening cites, you wish to cite to subsection (8)(a) of section 700.05. However, this subsection has been amended in its entirety and appears only in the 2020 pocket part.

   _____

10. In a legal memorandum, you have previously cited to a portion of the Maine state constitution, Me. Const. art. I, § 3. After several intervening cites to other authorities, you wish to cite to the same provision.

   _____

Chapter 9

COMPREHENSIVE CORE EXERCISE

After completing the first eight exercises, you are well on your way to mastering legal citation! Let's stop, catch our breath, and review what you have learned.

By now, you should know how to cite any case decided by a court in the United States, whether state or federal. Also, if you are citing a case to a state court and that state requires parallel citation to a state reporter and a regional reporter, you know how to construct that parallel citation. You also know how to use "*id.*" and how to formulate short forms for case citations.

Similarly, you know how to cite to any statute, state or federal. You are also comfortable using "*id.*" and short forms to refer to statutes that you have already referenced in a full citation.

With these skills, you can cite to most authoritative sources and produce a professional legal memorandum or court document. In the next exercises, we are going to introduce you to the concept of citation signals, which "signal" to your reader the importance of citations if the connection between the source and your proposition is not clear in the text alone. You will also learn how to add explanatory parentheticals to your citations to reinforce and clarify the importance of those citations. We will also explore other types of sources, such as books, treatises, law review articles, and legislative resources.

Before we continue marching on, you may want to try Exercise 9: Comprehensive Core Exercise, which will reinforce the skills learned in Exercises 1–8. To help you get back into the swing of things, the following is a list of common mistakes first-year law students make in basic citation:

- Forgetting to put a court designation in the court and date parenthetical when the reporter information is not sufficient.

- Guessing on the abbreviations in case names instead of checking Appendix 3.

- Omitting the volume and reporter information in a case short form: *i.e.*, "Casper, 99 U.S. at 310," **not** "Casper, at 310."

- Omitting the comma between the case name and the volume information in a case short form.

- Omitting the space between "F." and "Supp." and "2d" for cases reported in *Federal Supplement* ("F. Supp." and "F. Supp. 2d").

- Omitting a date parenthetical in a full citation of a statute.

Finally, remember your successful completion of these exercises does not mean that you should never consult the *ALWD Guide* again. Most student citation mistakes arise when students think they remember what the *ALWD Guide* says, but do not actually look up the rule. The best legal writers are not those that memorize the *ALWD Guide*, but those who know when to open it.

Exercise 9
COMPREHENSIVE CORE EXERCISE

Put the following information in correct *ALWD* citation form. Assume that the authority is being cited in citation sentences in a brief to the United States Supreme Court unless otherwise noted. For pinpoint citations, use a hyphen for page spans. This exercise reviews the skills you learned in Exercises 1 through 8.

1. Lawrence A. Schmid, Plaintiff, versus Robert A. Frosch, Administrator of NASA, Defendant. This case was decided in the United States District Court for the District of Columbia on January 30, 1985. This case is reported in volume 609, page 490, of *Federal Supplement* and in volume 36, page 1687, of *Fair Employment Practice Cases*.

    _____

    _____

2. On page 23 of your brief and in the same section of the discussion, you gave a full cite to the case in #1. On page 26 of your brief, you would like to refer to this case again, focusing your reader's attention on information beginning on page 495 of the opinion and continuing on page 496. You have cited to other cases in the interim. The case name does not appear in the textual sentence.

    _____

    _____

3. Section 26640 of the *California Government Code*, which you found in *West's Annotated California Code*. The statute appears in the 2020 pocket part.

    _____

    _____

4. You wish to cite again to section 26640 of the California Government Code in the next paragraph of your brief. You have cited to two cases since your last reference to section 26640. This is the only statute in your brief, so you would prefer to keep your short form as short as possible.

    _____

    _____

5. In a brief submitted to the Supreme Court of Virginia, you wish to cite to W.R. Grace & Company versus Maryland Casualty Company, et al. This case was decided in the Appeals Court of Massachusetts on September 30, 1992. It appears in volume 33, page 358, of *Massachusetts Appeals Court Reports* and in volume 600, page 176, of *North Eastern Reporter*, Second Series.

    _____

    _____

6. Section 3129(a) of title 7 of the *United States Code*, published in the 2018 main volume.

    _____

    _____

7.   Section 8, clause 8 of Article I of the Constitution of the United States.

_____

8.   One paragraph later, after citing to a federal statute, you wish to cite again to section 8, clause 8 of Article I of the Constitution of the United States.

_____

_____

9.   Ernest E. Jones, Terrence A. Larsen, and Herbert Lotman versus Raymond W. Smith and Peter S. Strawbridge. This case was decided by the Supreme Court of Pennsylvania on January 6, 1999. It appears in volume 734, page 862, of *Atlantic Reporter*, Second Series. The citation follows a direct quotation of material found on page 865 of the opinion.

_____

_____

10. Peter, Deputy Director, Patent and Trademark Office versus Nantkwest, Incorporated. This is a December 11, 2019 case from the United States Supreme Court. The docket number for the case is 18-8011. Assume the case has not yet been published in any reporter, and you would like to cite the slip opinion from the United States Supreme Court's website at https://www.supremecourt.gov/opinions/19pdf/18-801_o758.pdf. You wish to cite to page 2 of the slip opinion.

_____

_____

11. In your brief, you cited to the case in #10 [Peter, Deputy Director, Patent and Trademark Office versus Nantkwest, Incorporated. This is a December 11, 2019 case from the United States Supreme Court. The docket number for the case is 18-8011. Assume the case has not yet been published in any reporter, and you would like to cite the slip opinion from the United States Supreme Court's website at https://www.supremecourt.gov/opinions/19pdf/18-801_o758.pdf.] Now you would like to cite to that case again, but this time you would like to direct your reader's attention to information found on page 4 of the slip opinion. You have cited several other cases in the meantime. You have also cited a number of other cases involving the Deputy Director of the Patent and Trademark Office, so you need to craft your cite to eliminate confusion.

_____

_____

12. Federal Rule of Civil Procedure rule 20(a), dealing with permissive joinder of parties, published in the appendix to title 28 of the *United States Code* in the 2012 bound volume.

_____

_____

13. Section 4701 of title 16 of the *Delaware Code Annotated*. You found this on Lexis's Lexis Advance database. The database says that it is current "through 82 Del. Laws, ch. 219."

14. In a brief submitted to the Supreme Court of Virginia, you wish to cite to the State of Georgia versus Ronnie Jack Beasley, Jr. This case was decided by the Supreme Court of Georgia on July 30, 1998. It is reported in volume 269, page 620 of *Georgia Reports* and in volume 502, page 235, of *South Eastern Reporter*, Second Series. Assume Virginia rules only require a citation to the regional reporter for cases decided out of state.

15. In a brief to the Supreme Court of Georgia, you have previously cited to the case in #14 [the State of Georgia versus Ronnie Jack Beasley, Jr. This case was decided by the Supreme Court of Georgia on July 30, 1998. It is reported in volume 269, page 620 of *Georgia Reports* and in volume 502, page 235, of *South Eastern Reporter*, Second Series.] using a parallel citation form. You wish to cite to this case again on the next page of your brief after several intervening cites, focusing your reader on information contained on page 623 of the state reporter and 239 of the regional reporter. The case name is not mentioned in the textual sentence.

16. Section 810.02(b)(1)–(4) of *West's Florida Statutes Annotated*, which you accessed through the use of West's Westlaw database. The database says that it is current "through the 2019 First Regular Session of the 26th Legislature."

17. In the next sentence, you wish to cite to just subsection (3) of the Florida statute. You have not included any intervening citations.

18. Oliver Brown, et al., versus The Board of Education of Topeka, Kansas. This case was decided by the United States Supreme Court on May 17, 1954. It appears in volume 347, page 483, of *United States Reports*; in volume 74, page 686, of *Supreme Court Reporter*; and in volume 98, page 873, of *Lawyers' Edition*, Second Series.

19. On page 68 of your brief, you cite to the case in #18 [Oliver Brown, et al., versus The Board of Education of Topeka, Kansas. This case was decided by the United States Supreme Court on May 17, 1954. It appears in volume 347, page 483, of *United States Reports*; in volume 74, page 686, of *Supreme Court Reporter*; and in volume 98, page 873, of *Lawyers' Edition*, Second Series.] On page 72 of your brief and in the same section of the brief after citing to other authorities, you would like to refer to this case again, focusing your reader's attention on information on page 485 of U.S., page 688 of S. Ct., and page 875 of L. Ed. 2d. You have been referring to this case throughout your brief as *Brown*. The case name is not mentioned in the textual sentence.

_____

_____

20. The current Federal Rule of Evidence 803(2) published in the appendix to title 28 of the *United States Code* in the 2017 Supplement V.

_____

_____

Chapter 10

PRIOR & SUBSEQUENT CASE HISTORY

Now that you have mastered a basic case citation, you are ready to add a more advanced skill: prior and subsequent history. You probably have learned by now that one case may go through several levels of appeal in its life. At each level, the court reviewing the case may publish an opinion. Opinions issued by courts that review the case after the opinion you wish to cite are called *subsequent history*. Opinions issued by courts before the opinion you wish to cite are called *prior history*. As you read through this chapter, you may find helpful the examples in Rules 12.8 and 12.9. These rules tend to be pretty detailed and complex, but remember: you need not memorize any citation rules. You only need to understand how they work and where to find them so you can refresh your understanding.

To illustrate this, let's use the fictional case of *Bait v. Switch*. *Bait v. Switch* started out as a negligence lawsuit in federal trial court in the Northern District of Texas. Bait was awarded damages by the trial court, and the trial court issued an opinion. This opinion was reported in *Federal Supplement*. Switch then appealed to the Fifth Circuit Court of Appeals. The Fifth Circuit affirmed the trial court's judgment and also issued an opinion, which was published in *Federal Reporter*, Third Series. Finally, Switch filed a writ of certiorari to the United States Supreme Court. The United States Supreme Court denied certiorari, issuing an opinion explaining the reason for the denial. This opinion was reported in several reporters, including *United States Reports*. So we have three different courts that have dealt with this case and issued opinions. The Fifth Circuit Court of Appeals and United States Supreme Court opinions are *subsequent history* to the federal trial court opinion.

| N.D. Tex. | 5th Cir. | U.S. |

subsequent history

The federal trial court and Fifth Circuit opinions are *prior history* to the United States Supreme Court opinion.

| N.D. Tex. | 5th Cir. | U.S. |

prior history

The Fifth Circuit opinion has both prior and subsequent history—the federal district court opinion is prior history, and the United States Supreme Court opinion is subsequent history.

71

N.D. Tex.	5th Cir.	U.S.

prior history   *subsequent history*

You will find citations to prior and subsequent history by using a citator service such as *Shepard's*. You should receive instruction on how to use a citator in your legal research class.

Rule 12.8 governs subsequent history. Rule 12.9 governs prior history. The general rule for subsequent history is that any action listed in Rule 12.8(a) should be included when you cite an opinion in full. (This means that short cites should not include prior or subsequent history.) However, this rule has exceptions.

Include subsequent history unless . . .

- **the history is a denial or dismissal of certiorari or appeal and the cited case (not the denial or dismissal) is more than two years old**

  but: include denials of cert. or appeal if they are particularly important to your discussion, or

- **the history is history on remand, rehearing, or rehearing en banc.**

- **the history is a denial or dismissal of certiorari or appeal and the cited case (not the denial or dismissal) is more than two years old**

  but: include denials of cert. or appeal if they are particularly important to your discussion, or

- **the history is history on remand, rehearing, or rehearing en banc.**

The general rule for prior history is that it should be used sparingly and should be cited only when it is important for the point you are discussing.

When would prior history be important to a discussion? Let's go back to *Bait v. Switch.* Assume we want to cite the Fifth Circuit's opinion in *Bait v. Switch* because it is favorable to the point we are arguing. However, the Fifth Circuit opinion does not include as full a description of the facts in that case as the district court opinion does. If we wanted to analogize our facts closely to those of *Bait v. Switch* to argue that our client's case should be decided the same way the Fifth Circuit decided *Bait*, we might give the prior history of *Bait v. Switch* (the federal district court opinion) so we could use the lower court's description of the facts.

So now that you know **when** to give prior and subsequent history, you're ready to learn **how** to do it. Rules 12.8(c) and 12.9 tell us that the prior or subsequent history will follow the full citation of the primary case. This usually means that the history cite will follow the court and date parenthetical. However, if the primary case cite includes an additional parenthetical (for explanation, weight of authority, etc.—all things you will cover in Chapter 12), then the history cite follows that parenthetical.

A history cite must be introduced by an explanatory phrase. The explanatory phrases for subsequent history are listed in Chart 12.3. This chart also shows how the phrases should be italicized and punctuated. Notice that the comma following the phrase *should not* be italicized. The explanatory phrases for prior history are formed by converting the phrases in Rule 12.8(a) from "*-ed*" verbs to "*-ing*" verbs (*e.g.*, "affirmed" becomes "affirming"). Although a comma follows phrases introducing subsequent history, no comma follows phrases introducing prior history. These explanatory phrases give the reader important information about the relationship between the cases cited. For example, what if we want to cite *Bait v. Switch* (the district court opinion) for Proposition A, but it has been reversed in *Switch v. Bait* (the Fifth Circuit opinion) for the lower court's error on Proposition B? Although *Bait v. Switch* is no longer good law for Proposition B, it is still good law for Proposition A. To let your reader know that you are aware of the reversal but that it has no impact on your argument, you would introduce your subsequent history cite with the explanatory phrase "*rev'd in part on other grounds.*"

Sometimes, a case requires several history citations. If you give both a prior and a subsequent history citation, Rule 12.9 requires that the prior history be listed first and followed with the italicized word "*and*" and followed by the subsequent history.

Most of the subsequent history you will note will be in the cited case's direct line. For example, all of the opinions in the *Bait v. Switch* example involve the same parties and the same litigation. However, Rule 12.8(a) tells you to note as subsequent history cases that overrule a cited case, regardless of whether the cases are otherwise related.

What happens if the case name changes on appeal? Rule 12.8(e) covers this. If the names are simply reversed on appeal, then you do nothing. Cite the case name as it appears in the primary case you are citing and simply give a citation without a case name for the prior or subsequent history. The same is true if the history cite is a denial of certiorari.

But what if the first-named party changes on either or both sides? Not all parties that are involved in one phase of a case are necessarily involved in subsequent appeals. If you want to indicate a different name for a prior or subsequent history, add the phrase "*sub nom.*" to your explanatory phrase and give the case name along with its citation. When using "*sub nom.*" following an explanatory phrase, omit the comma that would ordinarily follow the phrase.

That's a lot of explanation, but the drafting is really not bad. Let's try an example. Because we are familiar with Bait and Switch, let's use their case and assume that we have the following citations to work with:

trial court:	*Bait v. Switch*, 111 F. Supp. 222 (N.D. Tex. 1994).
intermediate court of appeals:	*Switch v. Bait*, 333 F.3d 444 (5th Cir. 1994).
court of last resort:	*Switch v. Jones*, 555 U.S. 666 (1995).
unrelated case:	*Duck v. Cover*, 777 U.S. 888 (1997).

First, let's assume that we want to cite the intermediate court of appeals opinion in the Bait and Switch litigation. So, we start with that citation:

Switch v. Bait, 333 F.3d 444 (5th Cir. 1994).

We start with the general rule that we include subsequent history. So we consider whether to include the citation to *Switch v. Jones*. If *Switch v. Jones* was simply a denial of certiorari by the United States Supreme Court, we would not include it. Why? The decision in *Switch v. Bait* is older than two years. Therefore, the denial of certiorari would not be included. However, *Switch v. Jones* is not just a denial of cert.; let's say that when we look up *Switch v. Jones*, we discover that the Supreme Court heard the case and issued an opinion affirming the Fifth Circuit's decision in *Switch v. Bait.* However, it affirmed the Fifth Circuit on different grounds from those for which we intend to cite the case. First, we will need to turn to Rule 12.8(a) and Chart 12.3 to find out what explanatory phrase to use. We see *"aff'd on other grounds,"*—that looks like exactly what we need. Notice that we will replace the period at the end of the original citation sentence with a comma and save the period for the new end of our citation sentence.

Switch v. Bait, 333 F.3d 444 (5th Cir. 1994), *aff'd on other grounds*,

Notice that a comma follows the phrase, and remember that the comma *should not* be italicized.

Now it's time for the history citation. To name or not to name. Well, the party names are not simply reversed (*Switch v. Bait* and *Switch v. Jones*), and this is not a denial of certiorari. Rather, we have a subsequent history citation with a different name. So follow Rule 12.8(e) and add *"sub nom."* to the explanatory phrase and then give the case name along with the other citation information. Notice that no comma follows *"sub nom."*

Switch v. Bait, 333 F.3d 444 (5th Cir. 1994), *aff'd on other grounds sub nom. Switch v. Jones*, 555 U.S. 666 (1995).

Let's try it the other way around: cite *Switch v. Jones* with *Switch v. Bait* as prior history. The exact same explanatory phrase that we used for subsequent history will not work for prior history. Remember that Rule 12.9 tells us that we convert the phrase by changing the verb ending from *"-ed"* to *"-ing."* So we'll change *"aff'd on other grounds"* to *"aff'g on other grounds."*

Switch v. Jones, 555 U.S. 666 (1995), *aff'g on other grounds sub nom. Switch v. Bait*, 333 F.3d 444 (5th Cir. 1994).

Now, let's cite *Bait v. Switch* with all its subsequent history. Remember that Rule 12.8(c) says we can just attach the additional history to the citation. Let's assume that each court affirmed the court below it:

Bait v. Switch, 111 F. Supp. 222 (N.D. Tex. 1994), *aff'd*, 333 F.3d 444 (5th Cir. 1994), *aff'd sub nom. Switch v. Jones*, 555 U.S. 666 (1995).

Notice that we do not include a case name for the Fifth Circuit's opinion because the name is just a reversal of the cite before it (the primary cite of *Bait v. Switch*). However, we do include the case name for *Switch v. Jones* because it names different parties than the lower court opinions.

Okay, one more twist on Messrs. Bait and Switch. Let's cite the Fifth Circuit opinion, giving both prior and subsequent history. Remember that Rule 12.9 tells us to include prior history first and to join the subsequent history with the word *"and."* Again, assume that the case was affirmed all the way up.

Switch v. Bait, 333 F.3d 444 (5th Cir. 1994), *aff'g* 111 F. Supp. 222 (N.D. Tex. 1994), *and aff'd sub nom. Switch v. Jones*, 555 U.S. 666 (1995).

See? You're getting the hang of it! Let's assume that Bait, Switch, and Jones never went to the Supreme Court. They only got as far as the Fifth Circuit before they got tired of the whole thing. However, a few years later a similar case did go to the Supreme Court, and the Supreme Court's opinion in that case (*Duck v. Cover*) overruled what the Fifth Circuit had to say in *Switch v. Bait*. That would be important history to note any time you cite *Switch v. Bait*. You would do that according to Rule 12.8(a)(14):

Switch v. Bait, 333 F.3d 444 (5th Cir. 1994), *overruled by Duck v. Cover*, 777 U.S. 888 (1997).

Okay, now you're ready to make history on your own! Because these rules are so detailed, you may find the following checklists especially helpful in completing the exercise.

Checklist for Subsequent Case History

- Is there any reason not to include subsequent history?
  - The answer is yes if the subsequent history citation is . . .
    - an irrelevant denial of certiorari or other appeal on a decision older than two years, or
    - a history on remand, rehearing, or rehearing en banc.
  - Otherwise, continue . . .
- Have you replaced the period at the end of the primary citation with a comma (remember that the history cite follows the *entire* primary cite, even if the primary cite includes explanatory or other types of parentheticals)?
- Have you introduced your citation with an italicized explanatory phrase?
- Have you italicized the explanatory phrase but not the comma that follows it?
- Do you need to include the case name in the history cite?
  - The answer is no if . . .
    - the party names are simply reversed, or
    - the history cite is a denial of certiorari.
  - Otherwise, include the case name.
- If you included a case name, have you added *"sub nom."* to your explanatory phrase and deleted any comma following the phrase?
- If you included prior history in the citation as well, did you place the prior history first and join the subsequent history with *"and"*?
- If you have multiple subsequent history dispositions, have you listed them consecutively without the word *"and"* to join them?
- Did you end your full citation sentence with a period?

Checklist for Prior Case History

- Do you need prior history at all?
  - Is the earlier case significant to the point the primary case is being cited for?
- Have you replaced the period at the end of the primary citation with a comma?
- Have you introduced your citation with an italicized explanatory phrase converted from the subsequent history phrases in Rule 12.8(a)?
- Do you need to include the case name in the history cite?
  - The answer is no if . . .
    - the party names are simply reversed, or
    - the history cite is a denial of certiorari.
  - Otherwise, include the case name.
- If you included a case name, have you added *"sub nom."* to your explanatory phrase?

- If you included subsequent history in the citation as well, did you place the prior history first and join the subsequent history with "*and*"?

- If you have both prior and subsequent histories, have you joined them with "*and*"?

- If you have multiple prior histories, have you listed them consecutively without the word "*and*" to join them?

- Did you end your full citation sentence with a period?

Exercise 10
PRIOR & SUBSEQUENT CASE HISTORY

Put the following information in correct *ALWD* citation form. All cases are being cited in citation sentences in a brief to the United States Supreme Court. Although this exercise builds on the rules used in previous exercises, this exercise focuses on Rules 12.8 and 12.9. Unless the problem states otherwise, you should assume that case names are the same at each level of appeal. Remember that you must decide *whether* to include a history cite before you decide *how* to include one. The first case listed in each problem is the case you need to cite.

1. You want to cite AIG Annuity Insurance Company v. Law Offices of Theodore Coates, P.C., et al. This case is an April 6, 2012, federal case from the Tenth Circuit Court of Appeals. It is reported in volume 478, page 484, of *Federal Appendix*. The United States Supreme Court denied certiorari in October 2012. That denial is reported in volume 568 of *United States Reports* at page 932. You cite the case in a brief filed on October 3, 2020. The denial of certiorari is particularly important to your case's argument.

    _____

    _____

    _____

2. You want to cite Brad Bennett, et al., versus Marvin L. Plenert, in his official capacity as Regional Director, Region One, Fish and Wildlife Service, U.S. Department of the Interior, et al. This is a 1995 federal case from the Fifth Circuit Court of Appeals published in volume 63, page 915, of *Federal Reporter*, Third Series. This case deals with both First Amendment and Due Process issues. You are citing the case in support of a First Amendment issue. However, the case was reversed in 1997 on Due Process grounds. The reversal is published in volume 520, page 154, of *United States Reports*.

    _____

    _____

    _____

3. James Flanagan, et al., versus Gerald Ahearn, et al. This is a 1996 federal case from the Fifth Circuit Court of Appeals published in volume 90, page 963, of *Federal Reporter*, Third Series. The United States Supreme Court vacated this decision in an opinion published as *Ahearn v. Flanagan*, 521 U.S. 1114 (1996).

    _____

    _____

    _____

4. In a brief written on October 5, 2020, you want to cite Janice E. Hetzel versus County of Prince William. This is a 1996 federal case from the Fourth Circuit Court of Appeals published in volume 89, page 169, of *Federal Reporter*, Third Series. The petitioner requested that the United States Supreme Court hear the case on an issue unrelated to the issue for which you are citing the case. The Supreme Court denied certiorari in 1996 in a decision published in volume 519, page 1028, of *United States Reports*.

_____

_____

_____

5. You want to cite the case of Milton Knapp, Petitioner, versus Mitchell D. Schweitzer, Judge of the Court of General Sessions. This 1958 United States Supreme Court Case is published in volume 357, page 371, of *United States Reports*; in volume 78, page 1302, of *Supreme Court Reporter*; and in volume 2, page 1393, of *Lawyers' Edition*, Second Series. This case was overruled in 1964 by the case of William Murphy and John Moody, Sr., Petitioners, versus The Waterfront Commission of New York Harbor. That case is published in volume 378, page 52, of *United States Reports*; in volume 84, page 1594, of *Supreme Court Reporter*; and in volume 12, page 678, of *Lawyers' Edition*, Second Series.

_____

_____

_____

6. Edward Silva, Jr., versus The United States of America. This 1995 federal case from the Ninth Circuit Court of Appeals is published in volume 51, page 203, of *Federal Reporter*, Third Series. The United States Supreme Court first dismissed certiorari of this case in 1995. This dismissal is published in volume 515, page 1189, of *United States Reports*. The Supreme Court subsequently denied certiorari in 1995. The denial is published in volume 516, page 973, of *United States Reports*. Both the dismissal and the denial were on issues for which you intend to cite the Court of Appeals opinion and are, therefore, particularly important to the discussion.

_____

_____

_____

7. Haitian Centers Council, Inc., Plaintiffs-Appellants, versus Gene McNary, Commissioner, Immigration and Naturalization Services, Defendants-Appellants. This 1992 federal case from the Second Circuit Court of Appeals is reported in volume 969, page 1350, of *Federal Reporter*, Second Series. The United States Supreme Court reversed this decision as Chris Sales, Acting Commissioner, Immigration and Naturalization Service, et al., Petitioners, versus Haitian Centers Council, Inc., et al. This 1993 case is reported in volume 509, page 155, of *United States Reports*.

---

8. You wish to cite the classic substantive due process case of Peter Mugler, Petitioner, versus the State of Kansas. This 1887 United States Supreme Court case is reported in volume 123, page 623, of *United States Reports*. This decision reverses the decision of the Supreme Court of Kansas in this case. The Kansas Supreme Court's 1883 opinion is significant to your argument because it explains the issues more clearly and thoroughly. It is published in volume 29, page 252, of *Kansas Reports*.

---

9. Charles Carlisle, Petitioner, versus The United States of America. This 1996 United States Supreme Court case is reported in volume 517, page 416, of *United States Reports*. This decision affirms the 1995 decision of the Sixth Circuit Court of Appeals in this case. That 1995 opinion, which explains the issues more clearly and thoroughly, is published in volume 48, page 190, of *Federal Reporter*, Third Series.

---

10. United States of America versus Thomas M. Gaubert. This 1989 federal case from the Fifth Circuit Court of Appeals is reported in volume 885, page 1284, of *Federal Reporter*, Second Series. The Fifth Circuit reversed the 1988 trial court decision from the Northern District of Texas, located at volume 677, page 836, of *Federal Supplement*, which gives the best explanation of the issues in this case. The Fifth Circuit was later reversed by the United States Supreme Court in a 1991 decision reported in volume 499, page 315, of *United States Reports*.

Chapter 11

SECONDARY SOURCES

By now, you are highly proficient in citing any type of case law or legislative enactment. But you may want to cite to information located in other sources such as books, law reviews, and periodicals. You may even find yourself needing to cite to something more esoteric like a letter or a telephone interview. The *ALWD Citation Manual* dedicates many rules, beginning with Rule 20, to citing secondary sources such as these in their original media. Because you are already proficient in citing sources of positive law, citing these other print sources will be a snap.

However, you may be doing more and more of this type of research over the Internet or through an electronic database. Chapters 30-33 will explore how to cite sources found through these types of research. This chapter will focus on citing the original print source. Please review the rules mentioned below before attempting Exercise 11.

A. BOOKS

Rule 20 governs generally the citation of "books"—nonperiodic monographs. The basic citation form for a book will contain information regarding:

- the full name of the author or authors,
- the title of the book,
- the editor and/or translator, if any,
- the date.

If you would like to send your reader to a specific page or pages in the book, the page number would immediately follow the title.

Author, *Title* Pg. (Editor/Translator, Edition, Date).

Rule 20.1(b) tells you to give the author's name just as it appears. Unlike other citation systems you may have learned in your undergraduate or graduate studies, you do not rewrite the name to put the surname first. If the book has two authors, include both names joined by an ampersand (&) in the order that the names appear in the book.

Jonathan Harr, *A Civil Action* (1997).

Burton Silver & Heather Busch, *Dancing with Cats* (1999).

If the book has several authors, include all names as a series, with the names separated by commas and the last two names connected by an ampersand. Alternatively, if the work has three or more authors, Rule 20.1(b)(2) gives us the option of using the phrase "et al." after the first name.

J. Myron Jacobstein, Roy Mersky & Donald J. Dunn, *Fundamentals of Legal Research* 121 (7th ed. 1998).

or:

J. Myron Jacobstein et al., *Fundamentals of Legal Research* 121 (7th ed. 1998).

The next piece of information that your reader will need after the author is the title of the work. You should include the full title as it appears on the title page. Do not alter the title by abbreviating or omitting words, but capitalize according to Rule 3, which tells you to capitalize all words except articles, conjunctions, and prepositions. Rule 3 also tells us to always capitalize the first word in a title or subtitle and the first word following a colon.

Paul Alexander, *Salinger: A Biography* (1999).

Remember, the overriding concern in legal citation is that the reader should have enough information to find the exact source that you are citing. Therefore you will need to include the editor or translator, Rule 20.1(e)(1), even if the book has an author. The name of an editor will be followed immediately by the abbreviation "ed." and the name of a translator will be followed immediately by the abbreviation "trans." If a book has two editors or translators, then both names will appear and be followed immediately by "eds." or "trans." respectively. If a book has an editor and a translator, then the editor's name and designation appear first, followed by a comma and the translator information. Editor and translator information appears in the date parenthetical.

Gabriel Garcia Marquez, *Love in the Time of Cholera* 69–70 (Edith Grossman trans., 1988).

Sometimes, a book will not have a specific author, only an editor. In this situation, no author information will appear, and the editor information will appear in the date parenthetical.

The Antarctic Treaty Regime (Gillian D. Triggs ed. 1987).

Another piece of information that may appear in the date parenthetical is the publisher information. Rule 20.1(e)(2) tells us to add a publisher to the publication parenthetical only when citing a work published by someone other than the original publisher. Abbreviate words in the publisher name listed in Appendices 3(A), 3(D), or 3(E), and omit prepositions and articles not needed for clarity. Place the name after the translator or editor but before the year of publication.

The last piece of information you must include is the date of publication. Many books have only one publication date. However, some books are published in several editions. If you are citing to an edition other than the first edition, Rule 20.1(e)(3) tells you to include the edition number after any editor or translator information. This information is necessary for your reader to be able to consult a source that you are citing by page number. The page numbers of various editions will not be consistent, so your reader will need to know exactly what edition you are citing. Good legal writers cite to the latest edition, unless context requires otherwise.

J. Myron Jacobstein, et al., *Fundamentals of Legal Research* 121 (7th ed. 1998).

One last rule. If you are citing to a modern version of a work published before 1900, Rule 20.1(e)(5) gives you the option of including the original date of publication in a separate parenthetical at the end of your citation. For example, if you are citing a work of literature, you would include in the date parenthetical the name of the publisher and the date of the edition that you are citing. You would also include the original publication date in a separate parenthetical.

Thomas Hardy, *Tess of the D'Urbervilles* (David Skelton ed. 1978) (1891).

B. COLLECTIONS

Many books that you will cite will be collections of articles or essays. These sources follow the rule for shorter works in collection, Rule 20.3. In your legal citation, you must include:

- the full name of the author of the specific work that you are citing,
- the title of the specific work,
- the author of the collection, if any,
- the title of the collection,
- the page number on which the specific work begins,
- the specific page number cited,
- the editor and translator, if any,
- the numbered edition, if applicable, and
- the date.

Author, *Work Title*, *in Collection Title* Pg. (Editor/Translator, Edition Publisher (if not original), Date).

The name of the author will appear in ordinary roman type, and the titles of both the specific work and the collection will appear in italics.

Anthony A. Peacock, *Strange Brew: Tocqueville, Rights, and the Technology of Equality*, *in Rethinking the Constitution: Perspectives on Canadian Constitutional Reform, Interpretation, and Theory* 122, 125–156 (Anthony A. Peacock ed. 1996).

In addition, some frequently cited books have special citation forms. For example, Rule 20.5 gives you the citation forms for *The Bible*, the Koran, and the Talmud.

C. PERIODICALS

You will also on occasion cite to articles in periodicals and law reviews. Rule 21 provides rules on citing to all periodical materials. The basic form is similar to the form used for shorter works in a collection. In your legal citation, you must include

- the full name of the author of the article that you are citing,
- the title of the article,
- the volume of the periodical, if any,
- the title of the publication and any other pertinent volume or series information,
- the page number on which the specific work begins, and
- the date.

First, the author information will appear in your citation exactly like the author information in a book citation. Then, the title of the article will appear in italics, followed by a comma unless the title ends in a question mark or an exclamation point. Next, you will include the volume number of the periodical, if any. Law reviews are organized by volumes, which generally correspond to an academic year. However, each "volume" may be printed in separately bound publications with edition numbers. For example, Volume 22 of a certain law review may actually span three separately bound publications, which are usually soft-bound editions. Each publication may be given a number: Volume 22, No. 2. Once a volume is complete, the soft-bound numbered editions are collected and permanently bound as one volume. Therefore, the pages in each publication are numbered beginning with page 1 in Volume 22, No. 1 and ending with the last page of Volume 22, No. 3. Because of this numbering system, only the volume number and the page number are necessary to point your reader to the correct publication.

> Christine Hurt, *The Bluebook at Eighteen: Reflecting and Ratifying Current Trends in Legal Scholarship*, 82 Ind. L.J. 49 (2007).

Nonconsecutively paginated journals, however, require a different form and are governed by Rule 21.3. The format is generally the same as above, but without a volume designation. Instead, you will include the full date of publication before the page number on which the article cited appears. This information will enable your reader to find a specific issue of a nonconsecutively paginated journal. The page number follows the word "at."

> Author, *Article*, Periodical, Full Date, at Page.

> Lizzie Widdicombe, *Gwyneth's World*, New Yorker, Apr. 25, 2011, at 23.

If your periodical is a newspaper, then it is governed by Rule 21.3(f). The format is the same for non-consecutively paginated journals. You may want to include a parenthetical immediately after the periodical name with the place of publication. If the place of publication is well-known, then this step is not necessary.

> Michael S. Schmidt & Richard Sandomir, *Baseball Taking Control of Dodgers' Operations*, N.Y. Times, Apr. 21, 2011, at B2.

After your periodical abbreviation, simply insert the page on which the article begins.

On very rare occasions you will need to cite to a source that is unpublished in a written medium. Rule 27 covers interviews, letters, and memoranda, and Rule 29 covers forthcoming works and unpublished works, including working papers compiled on public databases.

D. ELECTRONIC SOURCES

Probably the most convenient feature of electronic databases is the easy searching of secondary sources. When you cite these sources to an electronic database, cite as you would to the printed resource, with an explanatory parenthetical containing the unique database identifier or the name of the provider and the database.

> Meredith R. Miller, *Contract Law, Party Sophistication and the New Formalism*, 75 Mo. L. Rev. 493 (2010), 75 MOLR 493 (Lexis Advance).

Rule 30.1 expresses a preference for print sources over electronic sources. However, if a source is only available on the Internet or if an Internet citation would facilitate reader access to the source, an electronic citation may be used.

1. Sources Available Only on the Internet

Rule 12.14(c) governs citations to cases available only on the Internet. When a case is available only on the Internet, Rule 12.14(c) tells you to include the case name, the docket number (if apparent), and a parenthetical with the court abbreviation and exact date (Month Day, Year). Following the court/date parenthetical, add a comma, and the URL for the website

Case Name, Docket No. (Ct. Month Day, Year).

San Antonio Area Found. v. Lang (Tex. Nov. 9, 2000), http://www.supreme. courts.state.tx.us/opinions991117o.htm.

Rule 31 focuses on websites on the World Wide Web, not particular sources that are also available on the Web. The citation form for any website will contain:

- name of author or owner,
- title of cited page and homepage or domain name,
- a pinpoint reference,
- URL,
- access or update information, if necessary, and
- exact date.

The placing of the date depends upon whether the website itself has a date or whether the only ascertainable date is the writer's visit to the cite. Rule 31.1(g) tells us that when the information will not change when posted, the date parenthetical goes after the domain name or homepage:

Dept. of Justice, *ADA Best Practices Toolkit for State and Local Government* (Apr. 29, 2011), http://www.ada.gov/pcatoolkit/toolkitmain.htm.

If the site does not give any date, give your reader the date you accessed the site in a parenthetical following the URL, using the phrase "last visited" before the date of access.

Community of Christ, *Years of Confusion and Disorganization (1844–1860)*, http://www.cofchrist.org/history/disorganization.asp (last visited May 2, 2005).

Rule 31.1(a) tells us that the "author" is either the person or organization that wrote the information being cited or, if not available, the host of the site. The title is also a little tricky. Sometimes you wish to refer to the site, so you use the title of the main "homepage." Other times, you may want to cite to a particular page or section. Then, you will include that title after the main title.

Michael Martinez, *CNN Justice, Garridos plead guilty in Jaycee Dugard kidnapping*, http://www.cnn.com/2011/CRIME/04/28/california.garridos.guilty. pleas/index.html (Apr. 28, 2011 8:51 p.m. EDT).

When giving the URL, include the entire address from the location you are citing.

If the URL will not take the reader directly to the source cited or if the URL is very long, Rule 31.1(e) allows you to include the protocol (e.g., http://), the domain name (e.g., www.stcl.edu), and the directory in which the file appears. After that information, you may identify keystrokes that will take the reader to the page you are citing. Rule 31.1(e) suggests keystroke identifiers "select," "path," and "search." Use "select" when the reader would have to answer a question of some sort to proceed further. Use "path" when the reader simply needs to follow a path of links (see example below). Use "search" when the reader can only retrieve the document by conducting a search with specific search terms. Separate the URL from the keystroke information with a semi-colon, and separate keystrokes from one another with a comma.

> Author, *Title*, URL; *keystroke identifiers* (Access or update information Month Day, Year).

> South Texas College of Law, *Practice Exams — Bergin*, http://www.stcl.edu; *path* Faculty/Professor Profiles/Kathleen A. Bergin/Link to Practice Exams.

2. Sources Available in Print and on the Internet

Rule 30.1 addresses sources that are available in both print and electronic format. In Rule 30.1, we see that we should cite to the print source if one is available. However, if the print source is difficult to locate, you might also want to give your reader a URL to find the information online. Rule 30.3 and Chart 30.1 tell you where to find out how to do this for various sources. For example, periodicals are governed by Rule 21.5, which tells us to cite the online version of a newspaper this way:

> Helene Cooper, *Bin Laden is Dead, U.S. Official Says*, N.Y. Times A1 (May 2, 2011), http://www.nytimes.com/2011/05/02/world/asia/osama-bin-laden-is-killed.html.

Exercise 11
SECONDARY SOURCES

Put the following information in correct *ALWD* citation form. All sources are being cited in citation sentences. This exercise focuses on Rules 20, 21, 28, and 33. You should follow the convention of placing one space after a colon, period, or question mark within a title.

1. "Can a Good Christian Be a Good Lawyer? Homilies, Witnesses, & Reflections," a book published in 1998 by the University of Notre Dame Press, Thomas A. Baker and Timothy W. Floyd, editors.

_____

_____

_____

2. A treatise "Modern Constitutional Law" by William J. Rich. You wish to cite volume 2 of the treatise at pages 157 to 159. This volume is part of the third edition of the treatise, and was published in 2011.

_____

_____

_____

3. "Terms of Engagement," a book by Clarke M. Neily III, published in 2013 by Encounter Books. You wish to cite page 93.

_____

_____

_____

4. "Crime and Punishment," a book by Fyodor Dostoevsky, originally published by a different publisher in 1865, translated by Constance Garnett and published in 1927 by Grosset & Dunlap.

_____

_____

_____

5. An article by Thomas C. Grey entitled "The Uses of an Unwritten Constitution," included in volume 2 of a compilation of articles entitled "The Rights Retained by the People: The History and Meaning of the Ninth Amendment," published in 1993 and edited by Randy E. Barnett. The article begins on page 199.

_____

_____

_____

6. An article entitled "Milberg Weiss: Of Studied Indifference and Dying of Shame" found on page 209 in volume 2 of the Journal of Business & Technology Law, published in 2007. The author of the article is Theresa A. Gabaldon.

_____

_____

_____

7. An article entitled "The Pink Tower Meets the Ivory Tower: Adapting Montessori Teaching Methods for Law School" by Emily Grant, found on page 603 of volume 68 of the Arkansas Law Review, published in 2015. You wish to focus the reader's attention on pages 607 to 608 of that article. Remember, most law journals are consecutively paginated.

_____

_____

_____

8. An episode of The Lawyerist Podcast, a (you guessed it) podcast. The episode itself is entitled "JDs and ADHD". It was hosted by Sam Glover, Aaron Street, Stephanie Everett and Marshall Lichty. It was produced on January 9, 2020. You accessed it at https://lawyerist.com/podcast/.

_____

_____

_____

9. An article appearing on page 11, section A, in the December 16, 2016 edition of the New York Times entitled "Migrant's Murder Case Grows More Tangled." The author of the article is Melissa Eddy.

_____

_____

_____

10. An article in the entitled "Inclusive Crowdfunding" written by Andrew A. Schwartz. This 2016 article appeared in the Utah Law Review for that year beginning on page 616. You wish to direct your reader's attention to page 618.

_____

_____

_____

11. An article in the December 16, 1999 issue of "Newsweek" magazine entitled "The World According to Google," by Steven Levy. The article begins on page 46. Because few people have access to older copies of Newsweek, you would like to include a parallel cite to the source on the web. You can access the article at: http://newsweek.com/world-according-google-140683.

_____

_____

_____

12. A blog post on SCOTUSblog by Amy Howe. The post appeared on January 22, 2020, and is titled "Argument Analysis: Justices divided in Montana school choice case." The post appears at https://www.scotusblog.com/2020/01/argument-analysis-justices-divided-in-montana-school-choice-case/

_____

_____

_____

Chapter 12

PARENTHETICALS

We know that legal citation serves two primary purposes: to give attribution to a source and to give locating information for a source. In addition, you have probably learned in your legal writing course that citations can also help make your writing more concise. Your citation can minimize or eliminate the need for some detailed explanation. For example, citations can give the year of decision and the jurisdiction of the case so that you do not have to give that information textually.

Instead of:

In 1995, the Texas Supreme Court held that false imprisonment is the willful detention of another without that person's consent and without authority of law. *Randall's Food Mkts., Inc. v. Johnson*, 891 S.W.2d 640 (Tex. 1995).

You can write:

False imprisonment is the willful detention of another without that person's consent and without authority of law. *Randall's Food Mkts., Inc. v. Johnson*, 891 S.W.2d 640 (Tex. 1995).

Citation parentheticals and signals provide additional citation tools for giving your reader useful information without including that information in a detailed discussion. In this chapter, you will learn how to use parentheticals. In the next chapter, you will learn how to use parentheticals with signals.

You have probably noticed in your legal reading that a great deal of information of several kinds is enclosed in parentheses at the end of some citations. This information falls generally into two categories: weight of authority and explanation. Weight of authority parentheticals give the reader information that indicates the precedential value of a cited case.

Welsh v. U.S., 398 U.S. 333 (1970) **(plurality)**.[1]

Explanatory parentheticals provide additional information to make clear to the reader the reason for the citation.

In re Marriage of Wood, 567 N.W.2d 680 (Iowa Ct. App. 1997) **(upholding an order modifying child support and requiring the father to contribute toward college expenses of the children)**.

While weight of authority parentheticals are only used with case citations, explanatory parentheticals may be used with any type of authority cited.

---

[1] Information appears in bold print in this book for highlighting purposes only. You should not format any part of your citations in bold print.

A. WEIGHT OF AUTHORITY PARENTHETICALS

Rule 12.10(a) and (b) explain how the case's precedential value should be included in a citation. Generally, two types of information indicate that the case does not have the same value as other cases decided by the same court—information that indicates the weight of the authority (*e.g.*, en banc, per curiam, 5–4 decision, dictum) and information that shows that the proposition cited is not the clear holding of the majority of the court (*e.g.*, dissenting, concurring, or plurality opinions). For example, dictum of the Supreme Court does not have the same value as a holding of the majority of the Court. Therefore, the fact that you are citing dictum of the Supreme Court is necessary to your reader's understanding of the value of your cited authority. You can indicate parenthetically that the information you have cited is dictum:

(dictum)

Similarly, a quotation of text from a dissenting opinion would not have the same weight as a quotation from the majority opinion. In that case, the parenthetical would look like this:

(O'Connor, J., dissenting)

In drafting weight of authority parentheticals, be guided by the examples in Rule 12.10(a) and (b).

B. EXPLANATORY PARENTHETICALS

Legal writers sometimes include information in explanatory parentheticals to citations to provide additional information that makes clear to the reader the relevance of the citation. Parentheticals provide a clear, concise, economical means of getting the maximum information to the reader with a minimum of detailed explanation. Their use is especially helpful when the writer does not really want to discuss the parenthetical information in text but still considers it necessary to help the reader fit the citation into the overall picture.

Rule 37.1 suggests using explanatory parentheticals with cases, and Rule 14.2(g) suggests using them with statutes. However, parentheticals can be used with any type of cited authority. Rule 37 gives the general rules for including explanatory parentheticals in citations to any source. The following discussion is applicable to all types of authority.

Most often, explanatory phrases begin with the present participle form of a verb (one that ends in *-ing*).

W. Wendell Hall, *Standards of Review in Texas*, 29 St. Mary's L.J. 351, 354 (1998) (**explaining** the difference between the standards of review for "no evidence" and "insufficient evidence").

Because the explanation is a phrase, it does not need a period within the parentheses. If the context of the citation makes a participle phrase unnecessary, a shorter phrase may be used:

The interviewer may be anyone authorized to investigate employment matters. *See, e.g., Black v. Kroger Co.*, 527 S.W.2d 794 (Tex. Civ. App.—Houston [14th Dist.] 1975, no writ) (**store manager**); *Safeway Stores, Inc. v. Amburn*, 388

S.W.2d 443 (Tex. Civ. App.—Fort Worth 1965, no writ) (**security guard employed by Safeway**).

In addition to explaining the relevance of a cited authority, Rule 37 tells us that parentheticals can also be used to explain the relationship between two sources. These are called commentary parentheticals:

La. Stat. Ann. §§ 2317, 2322 (1979) (**codifying** the rule in *Coulter v. Texaco, Inc.*, 547 F.2d 909, 913 (5th Cir. 1977)).

Meeker v. Hamilton Grain Elevator Co., 442 N.E.2d 922, 927 (Ill. 1982) (**quoting** *Bonebrake v. Cox*, 499 F.2d 951, 953 (8th Cir. 1974)).

C. ORDER OF PARENTHETICALS

Because case citations may include both weight of authority parentheticals and explanatory parentheticals, legal writers need a rule to guide them in ordering multiple parentheticals. Rule 37.2(b) requires that parentheticals that must be included as part of the citation appear before explanatory parentheticals. Because weight of authority parentheticals must accompany a citation, they should always be placed before explanatory parentheticals.

O'Connor v. Bd. of Educ., 449 U.S. 1301, 1306 (1980) (**Stevens, J., concurring**) (**affirming an order vacating a temporary injunction**).

If the citation also includes prior or subsequent history, Rule 37.2(a) requires that the parenthetical follow the source to which it relates.

Bennett v. Plenert, 63 F.3d 915 (5th Cir. 1995) (**holding that ranchers and irrigation districts were not within zone of interests protected by ESA**), *rev'd on other grounds*, 520 U.S. 154 (1997).

Mastery of the art of drafting explanatory parenthetical phrases will help you become a polished, professional legal writer—one who gets his or her point across in the fewest possible words. With a few well-chosen words in a parenthetical phrase, you will be able to communicate the crux of a case or other authority without discussing it at all in text.

D. DRY RUN

Let's walk through the process of figuring out (1) whether a citation needs a parenthetical and (2) if it does, how to put it together.

Suppose we want to cite *Smith v. Brown*, 123 U.S. 456, 467 (1970). We are citing Justice Euclid's concurring opinion. Concurrences do not have the same precedential value as majority opinions. Accordingly, Rule 12.10(a) indicates that we need a parenthetical phrase because the proposition for which the case is cited is not the majority opinion. The examples following 12.10(a) show that we should convey the appropriate weight of authority by adding the following parenthetical after the basic citation:

(Euclid, J., concurring).

Although this is a well-known case, we wish to cite it for one of its lesser-known propositions. Therefore, an explanatory parenthetical is also needed to make the citation's relevance clear.

So we must decide what to say and how to say it in the parenthetical. We are citing page 467 of the case on which Justice Euclid says in dictum that if X were Y, the jury's verdict would not have been allowed to stand. In our brief, we are arguing that the general rule represented by *Smith v. Brown* should not apply to our client's case because, on our facts, X *is* probably Y. How can we word that in an explanatory parenthetical so that it will be clear and concise?

First, the parenthetical phrase should probably begin with a present participle verb. We cannot use "holding" because the statement was dictum and appeared in a concurring opinion. Instead, we could use "suggesting" for our first word. For the rest, we can simply say "that if X were Y, the jury's verdict would not have been allowed to stand." Although we could quote the court's language in our parenthetical, the better practice is to paraphrase unless the actual words of the court are particularly memorable or concise.

Finally we must decide in what order to put the parenthetical phrases. Rule 37.2(b) guides us here. The weight of authority parenthetical must precede the explanatory parenthetical. So the completed citation would look like this:

Smith v. Brown, 123 U.S. 456, 467 (1970) (Euclid, J., concurring) (suggesting that if X were Y, the jury's verdict would not have been allowed to stand).

Notice the one space between each set of parentheses and the period at the end of the citation sentence *outside* the closing parenthesis.

Checklist for Parentheticals

- Have you checked each applicable rule (Rules 12.10, 14.2(g), and 37) to be sure you are including all the parentheticals you need?

- If the case has less precedential value than the court's clear majority opinions, have you included a weight of authority parenthetical that follows the examples in Rule 12.10(a) and (b)?

- If the relevance of the cited authority is not clear, have you included an explanatory parenthetical that follows the examples in Rule 37?

- If you have both weight of authority and explanatory parentheticals, have you placed the weight of authority parenthetical first?

- If your citation includes prior or subsequent history, have you placed the parenthetical(s) immediately after the court and date parenthetical of the cited authority as shown in Rule 37.2(a)?

- Have you left only one space before the parenthetical?

- Have you put the period ending your citation sentence *outside* the closing parenthesis?

Exercise 12
PARENTHETICALS

Put the following information in correct *ALWD* citation form. All sources are being cited in citation sentences. Assume that all citations will appear in a brief to a federal court. Although this exercise builds on the rules used in previous exercises, this exercise focuses on Rules 12.10, 14.2(g), and 37. Remember that each case name must be italicized according to Rule 12.2(a).

Note: In these problems, the wording for any explanatory phrase will appear in the text of the problem in quotation marks. Changes in wording will be read online as an error. This should not be construed as meaning that explanations have one "right" phrasing. This is simply a limitation imposed by the ICW's software.

1. Elliott Ashton Welsh, II, versus United States of America, a 1970 United States Supreme Court plurality decision (i.e., a case in which there was no majority opinion) reported in volume 398, page 333, of *United States Reports*.

    _____

    _____

    _____

2. A consolidated 1989 United States Supreme Court case, County of Allegheny, et al., versus the American Civil Liberties Union, Greater Pittsburgh Chapter, et al., and Chabad versus the American Civil Liberties Union, et al., City of Pittsburgh versus American Civil Liberties Union Greater Pittsburgh Chapter, reported in volume 492, page 573, of *United States Reports*. You want to refer specifically to material appearing on page 601 in the concurring opinion of Justice Sandra Day O'Connor. [*Hint: The American Civil Liberties Union is commonly referred to by its initials.*]

    _____

    _____

    _____

3. Geraldine Coulter, wife of James Coulter, and James Coulter, Plaintiffs-Appellants, versus Texaco, Inc., Texas Exploration and Production, Inc., and Rogers Louviere, Defendants-Appellees, an opinion of the Fifth Circuit Court of Appeals reported in 1997 in volume 117, page 909, of *Federal Reporter*, Third Series. You want to draw attention particularly to material on page 913 of the opinion "citing article 2317 of the Louisiana Civil Code Annotated, published by West in 1979." [*Note: You must properly draft the citation for article 2317 to include in your parenthetical.*]

    _____

    _____

    _____

4. Triad Electric & Controls, Inc., Plaintiff/Counter-Defendant Appellant/Cross-Appellee, versus Power Systems Engineering, Inc., et al., Defendants/Counter-Plaintiffs Appellees/Cross-Appellants, a 1997 opinion of the Fifth Circuit Court of Appeals published in volume 117, page 180, of *Federal Reporter*, Third Series. You want to quote material on page 192. You want to indicate in your citation that the court in Triad quoted the same material from a case titled T.J. Stevenson & Company, Inc., versus 81,193 Bags of Flour, etc., a 1980 Fifth Circuit Court of Appeals case published in volume 629, page 338, of *Federal Reporter*, Second Series. The quotation was taken from pages 369 and 370 of *T.J. Stevenson*.

---

5. You wish to cite section 777.011 of *West's Florida Statutes Annotated*, for the proposition that "establishing that presence is not required for responsibility as a principal in the first degree." This section appears entirely in the 2017 main volume.

---

6. Robert Michael Lawyer, Appellant, versus Linda Lorraine Lawyer, Appellee. This is a 1986 opinion of the Arkansas Supreme Court reported in volume 288, page 128, of *Arkansas Reports*, and in volume 702, page 790, of *South Western Reporter*, Second Series. You want to cite the dissenting opinion of Justice Hays, specifically the portion "stating that the legislative purpose behind § 34-1214 should not be frustrated." This statement appears on page 133 of *Arkansas Reports* and on page 793 of *South Western Reporter*, Second series. [*Note: Remember that your brief is to be filed in federal court.*]

---

7. In a brief to the United States Supreme Court, you wish to cite Henry F. Hartlove, Personal Representative of the Estate of Claude Faye Bass, versus the Maryland School for the Blind, a 1996 opinion of the Maryland Court of Special Appeals reported in volume 111, page 310, of *Maryland Appellate Reports*, and in volume 681, page 584, of *Atlantic Reporter*, Second Series. You want to cite this case specifically for its "holding that a litigant may not use a jury instruction as a vehicle for adding a cause of action" on page 315 of *Maryland Appellate Reports* and on page 587 of *Atlantic Reporter*, Second Series.

---

8. You wish to cite Lucent Information Management, Incorporated versus Lucent Technologies, Incorporated. This is a 1997 federal case from the district court for the District of Delaware. It is reported in volume 986, page 253, of *Federal Supplement*. Although you do not plan to elaborate on this case in text, you want the reader to know that its significance is its "holding that trademark ownership is acquired by adoption and use according to common law traditions." The Third Circuit Court of Appeals affirmed the district court's holding in 1998 in an opinion reported in volume 186, page 311, of *Federal Reporter*, Third Series.

_____

_____

_____

9. United States, Plaintiff-Appellee, versus John Javilo McCullah, Defendant-Appellant, a 1996 opinion of the Tenth Circuit Court of Appeals published in volume 76, page 1087, of *Federal Reporter*, Third Series. You want the reader to know that the significance of this case is the court's "remanding the case to the trial court for re-sentencing."

_____

_____

_____

10. "The Ethical Obligations of Prosecutors in Cases Involving Post-conviction Claims of Innocence," an article by Judith A. Goldberg and David M. Siegel of California Western School of Law. The article was published in Spring 2002 in volume 38 of the consecutively-paginated California Western Law Review. This article, which you want to cite because it is an article "outlining the significance of standards for reviewing issues arising under innocence-based post-conviction review statutes" begins on page 389. [*Note: The word "post-conviction" contains a hyphen even when printed on a single line.*]

_____

_____

_____

Chapter 13

SIGNALS

In the previous chapter, you learned that you can add parenthetical explanations to give your reader helpful information without making that information part of the text of your document. Citation signals are another tool you can use to give valuable information without a detailed explanation. Before reading the rest of this chapter, read Rules 35.2 and 35.3 so you will be familiar with the type and identity of the signals available to you. Reading through the explanations of the signals first will provide a context for the following discussion.

You have probably noticed citation signals in citations in the legal reading you have done already. Signals can properly be used with any kind of cited authority. The purpose of signals is to show the reader how the authority cited relates to what the text says and, in some cases, how it relates to other material in the same citation sentence. When you use a signal to describe the relationship between text and citation, the *ALWD Manual* strongly encourages a parenthetical explanation to elaborate on that relationship.[1]

Because the primary purpose of signals is to give the reader information without a detailed textual discussion, writers often take full advantage of signals by using one signal to introduce more than one source. If you intend for the same signal to apply to all sources cited in a citation sentence, the signal should not be repeated with each source—rather the signal will be presumed to apply to all sources following it (see example below). When signals introduce more than one source, the sources are separated by semi-colons and ordered according to Rule 36.3, Order of Specific Sources. Rule 36.3 tells us how to order different types of authority in a single citation sentence (*e.g.*, cases and statutes) and also how to order authority of only one type in a single citation sentence (*e.g.*, cases from several jurisdictions). For example, if a citation sentence includes both a case and a journal article, Rule 36.3 instructs that the case (Rule 36.3(d)) should be listed before the article (Rule 36.3(i)).

Contra City of Los Angeles v. Lyons, **461 U.S. 95** (1983); Brandon Garrett, Note, *Standing While Black: Distinguishing Lyons in Racial Profiling Cases*, **100 Colum. L. Rev. 1815** (2000).

On the other hand, if a citation sentence includes only cases, Rule 36.2 gives the order of cases within the sentences and Rule 36.2(d) says that cases decided by the same court should be listed in reverse chronological order.

See, e.g., Heath v. Jones, 817 S.W.2d 335 (**Tex. 1991**); *Cooper v. Smith*, 527 S.W.2d 898 (**Tex. 1975**); *Ludwick v. Miller*, 931 S.W.2d 752 (**Tex. App. — Fort Worth 1996**, no writ).

---

[1] So you can more easily locate and focus on the signals used in this chapter's examples, the examples do not include parenthetical explanations.

Writers can also maximize the use of signals by using more than one signal in a citation sentence. This is helpful when you want to describe both the relationship of the citations to the text and the relationship of the citations to one another. When using different signals in a single citation sentence, signals should appear in the order listed in Rule 35.3. In addition, Rule 35.4 requires that the different signals be separated by a semi-colon and a single space.

> *See State v. Michaels*, 642 A.2d 1372 (N.J. 1994); *see also Commonwealth v. Allen*, 665 N.E.2d 105 (Mass. App. Ct. 1996).

As with all other parts of a legal citation, signals have specific typeface rules. Introductory signals in citations are always italicized as provided in Rules 1.3(a) and 35.4. Remember, too, that a citation sentence has the same capitalization rules as a textual sentence: The first word must be capitalized. Therefore, a signal that begins a citation sentence is capitalized; otherwise, the signal is not capitalized.

> *See State v. Michaels*, 642 A.2d 1372 (N.J. 1994); *but cf. Commonwealth v. Allen*, 665 N.E.2d 105 (Mass. App. Ct. 1996).

Before you begin the exercise, let's go through an example of a citation that uses a signal and a parenthetical.

Suppose we write that "if a person is a farmer, then he is not a rancher." Although we don't have a source that directly says that, it is implied in the holding of *Rancher v. Farmer*, 888 P.2d 222 (Mont. 1985), that "farmers engage exclusively in one vocation." The question is, how can we indicate that without having actually to discuss the case in text? Easy: Introductory signals to the rescue!

First, look at Rule 35, the signal rule. Quickly scanning 35.3, we see that the signal "see" seems to fit our situation because it signals that the cited authority implicitly supports the textual proposition.

> *See Rancher v. Farmer*, 888 P.2d 222 (Mont. 1985)

We remember from Chart 35.1 that we should consider using an explanatory parenthetical anytime we use a signal. Parentheticals usually begin with an "*-ing*" verb that describes what the source does or says, so the first thing we want to do is choose a verb to begin our parenthetical. Because we are relying on what the court held in *Rancher v. Farmer*, we can begin the parenthetical with "holding" and then state the holding of the court:

> (holding that farmers engage exclusively in one vocation)

Remember that the explanatory parenthetical follows the completed citation, so our entire citation, complete with parenthetical, will look like this:

> *See Rancher v. Farmer*, 888 P.2d 222 (Mont. 1985) (holding that farmers engage exclusively in one vocation).

Remember to put a single space between the court and date parenthetical and the explanatory parenthetical. Also remember that the period at the end of the citation sentence goes outside the closing parenthesis.

And that's all there is to it!

Checklist for Signals

- Does your authority directly state the proposition, identify the source of a quotation, or identify an authority you mentioned in text?
    - If so, you can skip the rest of this checklist because Rule 35.2 tells us that no signal is required.
    - If not, you must have a signal, so continue.
- Have you selected the appropriate signal from Rule 35.3?
- Have you italicized the signal?
- Have you capitalized the signal if it is the first word of your citation sentence?
- Have you drafted an explanatory parenthetical to explain the relevance of your citation? (A quick review of the Chapter 12 checklist may be helpful.)
- Have you put the period that ends the citation sentence outside the final closing parenthesis?

Exercise 13
SIGNALS

Put the following information in correct *ALWD* citation form. All sources are being cited in citation sentences. Although this exercise builds on the rules used in the previous exercises, this exercise focuses on Rules 35 and 37. Determine what, if any, introductory signal you should use and what, if any, parenthetical explanation you should include.

Note: Although some citations lend themselves to alternative signal choices, be guided by the wording in the problem in choosing a signal. When the correct answer includes a signal, it will also include an explanatory parenthetical. As in the Parentheticals exercise, the wording for any needed parenthetical phrase will appear in quotation marks in the problem.

1. You write that "a father's failure to attend counseling mandated by court order is a sufficient change in circumstances to modify an earlier visitation order." Although your research did not find a case directly on point for this proposition, you did find a case "holding that a father's failure to use alternative dispute resolution procedures mandated in a prior court order constituted a change in circumstances sufficient to modify a support order." This case is Peter Q. Harris versus Bonnie L. Harris. This is a 1998 opinion of the Supreme Court of Vermont reported in volume 714, page 626, of *Atlantic Reporter*, Second Series. The holding in *Harris* supports your proposition only by analogy. Draft the citation that should follow your statement.

_____

_____

_____

2. In a brief to the United States District Court for the District of Kansas, you write that "a natural parent's right to custody is a fundamental right guaranteed by the Fourteenth Amendment." This proposition is supported implicitly by many opinions in which courts have rejected claims by non-natural parents on the basis that those parents' rights were not guaranteed by the Fourteenth Amendment. However, a citation to one of those opinions will be sufficient to make your point. You have chosen a Supreme Court of Kansas case to illustrate the point. That opinion is In the Matter of the Guardianship of Nolynn Glendon Williams, a minor child. This is a 1994 case "holding that absent extraordinary circumstances, the parental preference doctrine is to be applied." This case is reported in volume 869, page 661, of *Pacific Reporter*, Second Series. Draft the citation that should follow your statement.

_____

_____

_____

3. In a brief to an Alabama trial court, you quote directly from the case of Lisa Michelle Phillips versus Jack Lawrence Phillips. This is a Court of Civil Appeals of Alabama case decided on October 31, 1997, and reported in volume 705, page 512, of *Southern Reporter*, Second Series. Your quotation is taken from the dissenting opinion of Justice Crawley on page 513. Draft the citation that should follow your quotation.

---

4. In a brief to the Hawai'i Supreme Court, you write that the definition of farmland in Hawaii "includes land used for cane growing, fruit growing, and flower growing." This rule comes directly from section 155-1 of the *Hawai'i Revised Statutes* main volume published in 2018. Draft the citation that should follow your statement.

---

5. In a motion to dismiss filed in federal district court for the District of Connecticut, you write that "states disagree about whether grandparent visitation statutes may be invoked only in the course of other custody proceedings." You wish to offer support for this proposition by comparing two cases from courts that reached opposite conclusions. The first case is Frame versus Nehls "holding that the state's grandparent visitation statute did not apply in a paternity action because it was not an action for child custody." *Frame* is a 1996 Michigan Supreme Court case reported in volume 550, page 739, of *North Western Reporter*, Second Series. The second case is Castagno, et al. versus Wholean, et al., "reversing the dismissal of a grandparent's visitation petition for lack of jurisdiction in the absence of death, divorce, or a child custody proceeding." *Castagno* is a 1996 Supreme Court of Connecticut case reported in volume 684, page 1181, of *Atlantic Reporter*, Second Series. Draft the citation that should follow your statement. [*Note: Remember to order authorities using Rule 36.3(d).*]

---

6. In an office memorandum to your supervising attorney, you write that "grandparent visitation statutes began gaining popularity in the mid-1990s." To provide authority as helpful background information for this statement, you want to cite a 1995 law review note (as distinguished from a law review article) in volume 29, page 835, of the consecutively-paginated *Suffolk University Law Review*. The title is "Court-Ordered Families: An Overview of Grandparent Visitation Statutes." The note "providing a survey of grandparent visitation statutes from all states that have enacted them" was written by Michael Quintal. Draft the citation that should follow your statement.

———————————————————————————

———————————————————————————

———————————————————————————

7. In a brief to the Supreme Court of Wyoming, you write that "a state statute providing a five-year limitation period for paternity actions is constitutionally valid under the Equal Protection clause." In the interest of fairness, you wish to direct the court's attention to a concurring opinion in a 1996 Supreme Court of Wyoming case, State of Washington ex rel. D.A.A. versus C.J.H. This case is reported in volume 923, page 758, of *Pacific Reporter*, Second Series. The concurring opinion, by Justice Macy, "stating that, if properly brought before the court, the court would rule that a limitation period on paternity actions is unconstitutional because it discriminates between illegitimate and legitimate children" appears on page 763. This statement directly contradicts the position you have advocated in text. Draft the citation that should follow your statement.

———————————————————————————

———————————————————————————

———————————————————————————

8. In a brief to the Utah Supreme Court, you have quoted and discussed at length a case from the New York Supreme Court, Appellate Division, which raises the issue you are analyzing with facts that are virtually identical to your client's situation. To make the persuasive value of this case clear to the Utah Supreme Court, you wish to indicate at the conclusion of that paragraph that the law of the State of Utah is consistent with the New York law discussed. For this, you have chosen a 1997 Utah Supreme Court case "holding that, for the purpose of determining the validity of a trust, the interest of any beneficiary other than the grantor suffices." The case is Estate of Sharon W. Groesbeck versus David J. Groesbeck, and is reported in volume 935, page 1255, of *Pacific Reporter*, Second Series. Draft the Utah citation that should follow your discussion of the New York case.

———————————————————————————

———————————————————————————

———————————————————————————

9. In a brief to the Supreme Court of Nebraska, you write that "alimony is exempt from some limitations on garnishments." You inferred this statement from an opinion of the Supreme Court of Nebraska "holding that alimony was exempt from the 15% cap on garnishment of the ex-husband's Social Security benefits." This holding was articulated in Mary Jo Kropf, Appellee, versus Frederick J. Kropf, Appellant. This is a 1995 Supreme Court of Nebraska case reported in volume 248, page 614, of *Nebraska Reports*, and in volume 538, page 496, of *North Western Reporter*, Second Series. It is the custom in Nebraska courts to cite to both the official and regional reporter for Nebraska cases. Draft the citation that should follow your statement.

    _____

    _____

    _____

10. In a brief to a Nebraska trial court, you wish to cite *Hopkins v. Batt*. This is a 1998 Supreme Court of Nebraska case reported in volume 253, page 852, of *Nebraska Reports*, and in volume 573, page 425, of *North Western Reporter*, Second Series. You wish to indicate in your citation that this court reached the same holding as the case you have been discussing in text. Although *Hopkins* is distinguishable in some respects from the case you have been discussing, it provides additional support for the proposition you have just stated in text by its "citing section 42-377 of the *Revised Statutes of Nebraska*." That same statute is currently published in the 2016 main volume. Draft the citation that should follow the proposition in text. [*Note: You must properly draft the citation for section 42-377 to include in your parenthetical. It is the custom in Nebraska courts to cite to both the official and regional reporter for Nebraska cases.*]

    _____

    _____

    _____

Chapter 14

LEGISLATIVE & ADMINISTRATIVE RESOURCES

Legislative history and administrative resources can be seen as the bookends bracketing volumes of statutes. Legislative history documents reflect and give insight into the process by which a particular bill either becomes or does not become enacted law. At the other end of the process, the regulatory agencies promulgate regulations that help make the enacted statute operational. The documents generated by regulatory agencies and by the rest of the executive branch of government are collectively referred to as administrative resources. Accordingly, rules governing use and citation of legislative resources begin in Chapter 15, following Chapter 14, which covers enacted statutes. Chapter 18 contains provisions for citing administrative and executive resources. For convenience, this chapter of the ICW is divided into two subsections: legislative history resources and administrative resources.

A. LEGISLATIVE RESOURCES

This chapter and the accompanying exercises focus exclusively on federal materials. States vary widely in the publication of legislative materials, but many state legislative materials are patterned generally after the federal model. Therefore, the citation of legislative history follows the same general principles, whether federal or state.

In an increasingly codified legal system, statutory interpretation becomes a vital skill in many areas of legal practice. Often, a legal writer will rely on the intent of the legislature enacting a statute to properly interpret that statute. Legal writers look to the documents that are produced in the legislative process to determine that legislative intent.

To understand how to cite these documents, let's refamiliarize ourselves with the path a proposed law takes through Congress on its way to becoming "law." A proposed law may be presented in either house as a bill, a resolution, a joint resolution, or a concurrent resolution. For unenacted legislation, citation of these four types is essentially the same. Let's trace a wholly fictional bill from a Congressman's desk into the pages of the *United States Code*.

In the first session of the 112th Congress, Representative Blue introduces a bill he calls the Excellence in Legal Writing Act of 2011. This bill is the 911th bill introduced into the House of Representatives during this session, so the number given to the bill is H.R. 911. If our bill had been a resolution, the number abbreviation would be "H.R. Res. 911." Rule 15.1(b) lists abbreviations for all types of proposed laws.

H.R. 911, 112th Cong. (2011).

Rule 15.1(a) tells us that we may include the title of the bill or resolution. If you decide to include the title, place it at the beginning of your citation in ordinary type.

Excellence in Legal Writing Act, H.R. 911, 112th Cong. (2011).

Our bill is referred to the House Committee on Education, which in turn refers it to its subcommittee on Improvement of the Legal Profession, which then conducts hearings. The printed transcript of the hearing held September 11, 2011, shows on its cover the title "Excellence in Legal Writing Act: Hearings on H.R. 911 Before the Subcommittee on Improvement of the Legal Profession of the House Committee on Education." According to Rule 15.5, we cite to committee hearings by including the name of the title, which should include the bill number and the name of the subcommittee and committee, the number of the Congress, the page number, if any, and the year. If we cite to a particular part of the testimony at the hearings, we include a page number and also include a final parenthetical statement explaining whose testimony we are citing. The title is italicized, and we abbreviate the name of the committee according to Appendix 3.

Excellence in Legal Writing Act: Hearings on H.R. 911 Before the Subcomm. On Improving the Legal Profession of the Comm. on Educ., 112th Cong. 27–28 (2011) (statement of Mary Smith).

After hearings, the committee votes to recommend passage of our bill. The committee submits the bill, as amended, in a committee report. Committee reports are good sources of legislative history, including changes to the language of the bill and an explanation of the reasons behind the committee's recommendation. Committee reports are numbered sequentially. A citation to a report, according to Rule 15.7, will include the name of the house, the number of the Congress and the number of the report, a page number, and the year of publication. If the House report on our bill is the 83rd report this session, and the report is issued on October 13, 2011, a cite to page 5 of the report would look like this:

H.R. Rep. No. 112-83, at 5 (2011).

Other types of documents and reports may be issued concerning our bill. Citations to these documents will be exactly as above, except for a different "Rep." abbreviation. Rule 15.7(b) lists the abbreviations for these various documents.

For some but not all bills, House and Senate reports, as well as recent conference reports, are reprinted, together with the related bill, in the *United States Code Congressional and Administrative News* (abbreviated U.S.C.C.A.N. and informally called "you–scan"). Some reports are also reprinted in the *Congressional Record*. When your legislative resource is available in U.S.C.C.A.N., you should include a reference to it, as provided in Rule 15.7(f).

H.R. Rep. No. 112-83, at 5 (2011), *reprinted in* 2011 U.S.C.C.A.N. 6144.

Now, back to our bill! Our bill now goes to the floor of the House for a vote. The bill is debated on the floor of the House, and the *Congressional Record* includes a transcript of the debate. The *Congressional Record* is published daily during each legislative session. At the end of each session, all daily editions are published in a permanent, bound edition. The rule governing citation to the debate is Rule 15.10. If the debate is published on page 23,251 of volume 143 of the *Congressional Record*, our citation would look like this:

143 Cong. Rec. 23,251 (2011).

If we were citing the debate before the permanent edition of that volume of the *Congressional Record* became available, Rule 15.10 tells us that we would cite to the daily edition. That means that we would give the full date, remembering to abbreviate the month as shown in Appendix 3, and that information would become part of the parenthetical. Notice that an "H" precedes the page number in the daily edition citation because the daily editions are separated into House and Senate proceedings, each with its own consecutive pagination. The page numbers in the separate volumes are preceded by either an "H" or an "S" so you will know which section of the daily edition, House or Senate, to consult:

143 Cong. Rec. H12,345 (daily ed. Nov. 15, 2011).[1]

Our bill passes the House! After approval by the House of Representatives, the bill is sent to the Senate for consideration. The Senate will have similar committee hearings and debates on our bill. Once the Senate also passes it, it is assigned a session law number. Most federal session laws are called Public Laws, and Public Law numbers reflect simply the number of the Congress, here the 112th, and the chronological order of the enactment. The law we are tracing is the 205th law enacted by the 112th Congress; therefore, its session law number is Public Law 112-205, abbreviated "Pub. L." as shown in Rule 14.6(b). The session law citation is as follows:

Excellence in Legal Writing Act, Pub. L. No. 112-205 (2011).

Federal session laws are compiled in *United States Statutes at Large*, which, as Rule 14.6(d) indicates, is abbreviated "Stat." Our newly enacted statute appears on page 683 of volume 127 of *United States Statutes at Large*. When the statute appears in that source, its citation will include that information:

Excellence in Legal Writing Act, Pub. L. No. 112-205, 127 Stat. 683 (2011).

When you know where the enacted statute will be codified (usually this information is part of the enacted bill itself), include that information parenthetically in its citation, as Rule 14.6(g) provides. Thus if our statute will be codified as section 1331 of title 53 of the *United States Code*, its citation will reflect this information:

Excellence in Legal Writing Act, Pub. L. No. 112-205, 127 Stat. 683 **(2011) (to be codified at 53 U.S.C. § 1331).**

Once the act is codified, you will ordinarily cite it as a statute according to the provisions of Chapter 14. However, occasionally you may have a specific reason to cite the bill or the session law. For example, you may wish to cite to the session law when it is codified in many scattered sections or titles of the official code. In addition, you would also want to cite to the original bill to show amendments and to document legislative history. Rule 15.3 tells you to cite enacted bills and joint resolutions just as you would cite unenacted bills and joint resolutions. Rule 15.4 gives you special guidance for citing enacted simple resolutions and concurrent resolutions.

---

[1] On LexisNexis and WESTLAW, all *Congressional Record* cite page numbers are preceded by "H" or "S" even after the document is printed in the permanent edition. However, your citations should follow the ALWD rule of eliminating the "H" or "S" once it is published in the permanent edition.

B. ADMINISTRATIVE RESOURCES

Just as enacted statutes are positive law, so are the administrative rules and regulations that implement them. Administrative regulations originate with the agencies and departments of the executive branch of government. Take a couple of minutes now to scan the provisions of Rule 18 and familiarize yourself with its contents.

The primary sources of federal administrative materials are the *Code of Federal Regulations* and the *Federal Register*. Rule 18.1 governs final rules and regulations, published in the C.F.R., and Rule 18.3 deals with citing proposed rules and regulations found in the daily editions of the *Federal Register*, as well as administrative notices of numerous kinds.

The C.F.R. is the official compilation of codified rules and regulations and is organized and cited much like the *United States Code*. Both are arranged topically into titles; however, the titles of the U.S.C. and the C.F.R. do not parallel one another. Otherwise, the citation forms are also quite similar. If a rule or regulation has a familiar name, then you may wish to include the name at the beginning of your citation in ordinary type. Just as the title number precedes the abbreviation U.S.C., so the title number of the regulation precedes the abbreviation C.F.R. And just as the section number of the statute follows the code abbreviation, so the regulation section or part number follows its code abbreviation. Also like statutory citations, a citation to a regulation needs a date. This date is the date on the most current volume of the C.F.R., not the date of adoption of the rule or regulation.

Statute: Employee Retirement Income Security Act of 1974, 29 U.S.C. § 1132 (2006).

Regulation: Employee Welfare Benefit Plan, 25 C.F.R. § 2510.3-1 (2011).

or

25 C.F.R. § 2510.3-1 (2011).

Rule 18.1 tells us to cite final rules to the *Code of Federal Regulations* if possible, or to the *Federal Register* if not, indicating parenthetically where the new rule will be codified. (If all this sounds familiar to you, aren't you glad you learned the federal statutory citation material so well?) Each title of the *Code of Federal Regulations* is revised each year, but not all at the same time. The revisions are spread out over four quarterly publication dates, January, April, July, and October. The date of each volume of *Code of Federal Regulations* appears on the cover.

As you have learned (or soon will learn) in legal research, when an administrative agency proposes (or promulgates) a regulation, notice of that proposed regulation is published in the *Federal Register*. When a regulation is adopted in its final form, it will appear first in the *Federal Register* and then in the *Code of Federal Regulations*. The *Federal Register* contains administrative notices, proposed regulations, and other announcements. Rule 18.3 tells us to cite proposed rules, regulations and notices the same way we would cite a final regulation, except that we must include the exact date of the cited *Federal Register* volume.

Incentive-Based Compensation Arrangements, 76 Fed. Reg. 21,170 (Apr. 14, 2011).

If you cite only a part of a rule, as with a pinpoint citation to any source you must indicate in the full citation not only the beginning page of the rule, but also the specific page on which the cited material appears. The following pinpoint citation to a final rule demonstrates this:

Grants to Combat Violent Crimes against Women on Campuses, 64 Fed. Reg. 39,774, 39,777 (July 22, 1999).

Although most of the administrative materials you will have occasion to cite in law school and in your law practice will probably be of the regulatory type, presidential proclamations, Attorney General opinions, and executive orders are also administrative materials, and we cite them according to Rules 18.7, 18.9, and 18.10. Proclamations and executive orders that are currently in force are published in the C.F.R. If a source is not published in the C.F.R. you may cite to the *Federal Register*.

Exec. Order No. 12,781, 3 C.F.R. 373 (2009).

Short forms for citations to C.F.R. and the *Federal Register* are discussed in Rule 18.2 and Rule 18.4, which parallel short forms for statutes. For example, if you had already given a full citation for the following final rule:

18 C.F.R. § 385 (2011).

then a later citation to the same section after intervening cites would take the following form:

18 C.F.R. § 385.

See how easy it all is? Take it away, citation wizards!

Exercise 14
LEGISLATIVE & ADMINISTRATIVE RESOURCES

A. LEGISLATIVE RESOURCES

Put the following information in correct *ALWD* citation form. All sources are being cited in citation sentences in a brief to be filed in a federal court of appeals. Although this exercise builds on the rules used in the previous exercises, this exercise focuses on Rules 14 and 15.

1. You want to quote some testimony from a committee hearing. The title on the cover of the published document is "California Desert Lands: Hearings on H.R. 518 and H.R. 880." The hearing was before the Subcommittee on National Parks, Forests and Public Lands of the House Committee on Natural Resources. The language you are quoting appears on page 96. The hearing took place on June 15, 1993, during the first session of the 103d Congress.

   _____

   _____

   _____

2. In a discussion of the legislative history of the Truth in Lending Act, you cite a session law called the Truth in Lending Class Action Relief Act of 1995, published in volume 109 of *United States Statutes at Large* at page 161. The bill was passed in 1995 and given the public law number 104-12. You would like to include the name of the act.

   _____

   _____

   _____

3. You want to use the definition of the term "federal mandate" that appears on page 6 of a Senate report, number 104-1, published on January 11, 1995. The report was reprinted in the 1995 volume of the *United States Code Congressional and Administrative News* beginning at page 4; the precise language you are quoting appears on page 10 of that publication.

   _____

   _____

   _____

4. In a brief you wish to cite to a statement made by Representative Richard Gephardt on March 24, 1999, during the House debate on H.R. 104-1141. The statement is published in the permanent edition of volume 145 of the *Congressional Record* of that date. The portion of the debate you are citing appears on page 1617.

   _____

   _____

   _____

B. ADMINISTRATIVE RESOURCES

Put the following information in correct *ALWD* citation form. All cases are being cited in citation sentences in a brief to be filed in a federal court of appeals. Although this exercise builds on the rules used in previous exercises, this exercise focuses on Rule 18.

1. In your brief you are citing a rule concerning prohibitions on political activities applicable to attorneys and staff attorneys of the Legal Services Corporation. The rule is found in title 45 of the *Code of Federal Regulations*, at section 1608.6. The current volume of title 45 was published in 2018.

   _____

   _____

   _____

2. You want to cite a number of regulations of the National Labor Relations Board that appear in the 2018 volume of title 29 of the *Code of Federal Regulations* as sections 102.3 to 102.6.

   _____

   _____

   _____

3. You are citing a rule concerning pilot project exemptions to certain rules implementing the National School Lunch Program. It appears in title 7 of the *Code of Federal Regulations* as section 210.19 in part 210. The publication date of title 7 is 2019. You accessed this edition online in the official Federal Digital System at https://www.govinfo.gov/content/pkg/CFR-2019-title7-vol4/pdf/CFR-2019-title7-vol4-subtitleB.pdf.

   _____

   _____

   _____

4. You are citing a proposed rule of the Nuclear Regulatory Commission proposed on Tuesday, November 19, 2019, and published in volume 84 of the *Federal Register*, beginning at page 63,816. The title of the rule is "Power Reactor In-Core Monitoring."

   _____

   _____

   _____

5. You are citing a proposed rule published on Tuesday, December 17, 2019 in the *Federal Register*, volume 84, at page 68,816. The title of the proposed rule is "National Bioengineered Food Disclosure Standard; Validation of Refining Processes". It will eventually be codified in title 7 of the *Code of Federal Regulations*, part 66.

---

6. You are citing to Presidential Proclamation number 7623, made by President George W. Bush on Veterans Day, November 6, 2002. This proclamation appears in volume 67 of the *Federal Register* on page 68,751

---

7. You wish to cite to Executive Order No. 13,268, issued by President George W. Bush on July 2, 2002, terminating the national emergency declared on July 4, 1999 with respect to the Taliban. This order does not appear in the *Code of Federal Regulations*. However, it appears in volume 67 of the *Federal Register* on page 44,751.

Chapter 15

WHEN DO I CITE?

We have often found that in teaching our students the intricacies of legal citation rules, we need to stop and focus on the most important citation rule: The rule that tells us when we must cite! Knowing when to cite can be tricky until you have some experience in writing legal memoranda, court documents, or a scholarly paper. You probably have brought some citation placement experience with you from your undergraduate or graduate work. For better or worse, legal writing requires very precise and usually frequent citation of the propositions in our legal writing—probably more precision and frequency than writing in other fields. Rule 34 of the *ALWD Citation Manual* will be a very helpful reference to you for determining when to include a citation.

The general rule of thumb for legal memoranda and court documents is that you need a citation for every fact, thought or opinion that comes from another source (not you or your facts). Rule 34.2 reminds us of this basic tenet. You need a citation even if you are not quoting. The purpose of your citation is to enable your reader to go to a specific page of a specific source and find support for the sentence preceding the citation. If you are detailing the facts of a case or the holding of a case, then you need a citation to that case, whether you are quoting or paraphrasing. If you are quoting or paraphrasing a statute or regulation, then you need a citation. If you are making a proposition about the state of the law generally, then you need a citation to a source that supports that proposition. If you are providing your reader with a rule that you have synthesized from several sources, then you need cites to those sources. Here are some examples of the types of sentences you will write in a legal memorandum or a court document that would need citations:

> In our jurisdiction, courts look to numerous factors when determining whether an individual can establish ownership by adverse possession. *Belotti v. Bickhardt*, 127 N.E. 239 (N.Y. 1920).

> The Court of Appeals of New York held that the defendant's possession must be hostile and under a claim of right; the possession must be actual; the possession must be "open and notorious"; the possession must be exclusive; and the possession must be continuous for a period of twenty years. *Belotti v. Bickhardt*, 127 N.E. 239, 241 (N.Y. 1920).

> The defendant used and rented all portions of a building, a portion of which was built on property owned by the plaintiff. *Belotti v. Bickhardt*, 127 N.E. 239, 240 (N.Y. 1920).

Usually, your entire sentence will be supported by a single citation. In these cases, your citation will immediately follow your textual sentence in a separate *citation sentence*. The examples above are citation sentences. (Notice that they appear as regular sentences and are not in parentheses, unlike other humanities citation systems.)

However, Rule 34.1(b) tells us that if only part of our sentence relates to the citation, then we need to insert a *citation clause* immediately following that part of the sentence. If the clause appears between text, then it is set off by commas. If the clause appears at the end of the sentence, it is set off by one comma and ends the sentence with a period.

> Although prior to 1962, the required period for adverse possession was twenty years, *Belotti v. Bickhardt*, 127 N.E. 239 (N.Y. 1920), the current statutory period is ten years, N.Y. Real Prop. Actions & Proc. Laws § 501 (McKinney 1979).

Rule 34.1(c) gives us a third citation device: the embedded citation. With an embedded citation, the full cite of a source is incorporated into the text of your sentence, and you do not add any citation clause or citation sentence.

> In *Belotti v. Bickhardt*, 127 N.E. 239 (N.Y. 1920), the court looked to several factors to determine whether an individual can establish ownership by adverse possession.

Although both the citation clause and the embedded citation are unavoidable at times, some legal readers do not like the interruption of the flow of the text. For this reason, use these citation techniques with discretion. You may choose to rewrite your sentence to utilize the preferred citation sentence.

Note, however, that you do not need a citation when detailing your own facts or even applying a previously cited rule to your facts. If in doubt, ask yourself: "If my reader turns to this page of this source, would the reader find support for this statement?" Here are some examples to illustrate:

> Tina Trespasser, our client, should be able to show that she meets all five of the requirements to prove adverse possession.

> Tina, like the defendant in *Belotti*, has continuously occupied the land in question and earned income from it.

Notice that some of the examples in this chapter cite to the first page of the case only, while others pinpoint the location of specific material cited. When authority is used to represent a rule of law (*e.g.*, a landmark decision like *Roe v. Wade* for the right to privacy), then the citation does not necessarily require a pinpoint. However, when your citation follows facts or reasoning from the case, a pinpoint citation is needed to help your reader find the information cited.

Now that you know how to cite and when to cite, you're all set!

Exercise 15
WHEN DO I CITE?

For this exercise, you will use a set of facts about a fictitious client and two actual cases. You will be given sentences taken in order from a hypothetical discussion section in a legal memorandum. You will need to decide whether each sentence requires a citation to one of the given cases.

If you determine that the sentence does not require a citation, then simply leave the space after the sentence blank. (If you are doing this exercise on the website, then type "no citation" in the solution box blank and click "submit."). If you determine that the sentence does require a citation, then simply type either "Exxon" or "Gonzales" in plain type, as applicable.

This exercise emphasizes the placement, rather than the form, of citation. Accordingly, when a citation is required, you should type "Exxon" or "Gonzales" regardless of whether a full, short, or "*id.*" form ought to be used and regardless of whether a pinpoint cite ought to be included.

Facts: Your client is Kendall Loeb. Mr. Loeb lives across the street from a convenience store, The Quik Shop. On August 7, 2001, in the parking lot of the store, Mr. Loeb had an argument with another customer. The customer threatened to kill him and then sped out of the parking lot. Mr. Loeb asked the store attendant, who heard the threat, to call the police, and the attendant refused. As Mr. Loeb was walking back to his house, the customer returned in his truck and hit Mr. Loeb with the truck. Mr. Loeb has filed suit against the store for negligently failing to protect him from the other customer's assault.

Cases: *Exxon Corp. v. Tidwell*, 867 S.W.2d 19 (Tex. 1993). This Texas Supreme Court opinion states the general rule that a landowner has no duty to protect invitees on the premises from criminal acts of third parties. An exception to this rule occurs when the owner both has direct control of the safety and security of the premises and could have foreseen the criminal acts. This case does not focus on the "foreseeability" exception. The rule and exceptions are stated on page 20 of the court's opinion.

Cases: *Gonzalez v. S. Dallas Club*, 951 S.W.2d 72 (Tex. 1992). This case focuses on the "foreseeability" exception. The court specifies the circumstances in which a criminal act would be foreseeable. The court's holding and rationale are on page 76. The facts appear on page 73.

1. Mr. Loeb can prove that the criminal actions of the perpetrator were foreseeable as a matter of Texas law.

---

2. In Texas, a business owner will be liable for criminal actions of a third party that occur on the premises only if the actions were foreseeable by the owner.

---

3.   In addition, the business owner must have direct control over the safety and security of the premises in order to be liable in a failure to protect cause of action.

4.   In our case, Mr. Loeb will have to prove that the assault of the customer was foreseeable by the store clerk.

5.   In Texas, a criminal act of a third party is foreseeable if the owner or his agent knew or should have known either that (a) a specific confrontation would result in an assault once the parties left the premises or (b) the assault was a common type of crime that occurred in that area.

6.   Because the area was not a high-crime area, Mr. Loeb will have to prove that the store clerk knew or should have known that the confrontation between Mr. Loeb and the customer would result in an assault after Mr. Loeb left the store.

7.   In a Texas Supreme Court case *Gonzalez v. South Dallas Club*, the court held that an owner cannot foresee a later criminal act when he takes all necessary steps to provide for the safety of a customer exiting the premises.

8.   In *Gonzales*, the owner escorted a nightclub patron to her car and watched her drive safely away.

9.   Unlike the owner in *Gonzales*, the Quik Shop clerk refused to take any steps to provide for the safety of Mr. Loeb, even when the clerk was told that Mr. Loeb was in danger.

10.   Because the resulting assault was foreseeable and because the clerk refused to take any steps to safeguard Mr. Loeb, the court should find the Quik Shop negligent for failing to protect its invitee, Mr. Loeb.

Chapter 16

COURT DOCUMENTS: TRIAL & APPELLATE

So far, we've focused on how to cite authority. However, the law isn't the only material that comes from external sources. The facts also come from external sources. And just as legal readers use the citations in your document to locate and verify the authority you've cited, legal readers also need citations to locate and verify the facts and allegations to which you apply the law in your analysis. Those facts are recorded in a variety of court documents, and those court documents compose what's called the "record" of the case. To fully understand what the record is, you need to first know how documents make their way into the record. Although specific practices vary from jurisdiction to jurisdiction, the general practice of accumulating the record is similar across the country. This chapter will use civil actions in federal courts for illustration.

The first document filed in a case is, of course, the complaint. When a document is "filed," that means it has been submitted to the clerk's office for that court. The clerk's office will start a file for that case and assign it a number. That number is called the "docket number." From that point forward, all documents filed in that case should have that number printed on them, and all documents will be placed in that file in chronological order behind the complaint. Therefore, the next document in the file behind the complaint will likely be some responsive pleading by the defendant. After the initial pleadings in the case, the other documents listed in Rule 25 may be filed.

A. CITING DOCUMENTS DURING THE TRIAL PROCESS

While the case makes its way through the trial process, the parties may want to refer back to documents already filed. For example, a Motion for Summary Judgment might refer back to facts stated in the Complaint. When the facts from the Complaint are referenced, the writer will need to cite the Complaint. To cite documents filed in the same case, you would consult Rule 25. Read through Rule 25 before continuing with this chapter.

1. Full Citation Form

A basic court document citation consists of the abbreviated document name, a pinpoint reference to the material cited, and the exact date of the document.

The first part of a court document citation is the abbreviated name of the document. For guidance in forming abbreviations for court documents, use Appendix 3(G). Appendix 3 contains abbreviations for words commonly found in court document titles. In addition to abbreviating words, you may eliminate articles and prepositions in the document name when they are not needed for clarity.

> Defendant's Brief in Support of Motion for
> Summary Judgment

becomes: Def.'s Br. Supp. Mot. Summ. J.

                Plaintiff's Motion to Compel
becomes: Pl.'s Mot. Compel

When a person's name is part of the document title, the name should be included in the citation:

                Affidavit of Carlton Wells
becomes: Aff. Carlton Wells

The second part of the court document citation is the pinpoint reference for the material cited. Rule 25.2(b) tells you to use the most specific reference possible.

cited by page number   Pl.'s Br. Support Mot. Quash Subpoena 15
cited by paragraph number   Def.'s Ans. ¶ 4
cited by item number   Pl.'s Req. Prod. No. 7

If you have a choice between citing by paragraph number or page number, consider which reference would be most helpful to your reader. If a document is one or two pages long (like an affidavit or short motion), reference the paragraph number to help the reader immediately pinpoint the information cited.

     Mot. Dismiss ¶ 4.

     Pl.'s Mot. Compel ¶¶ 9-12.

However, if the document is more than two pages and the paragraphs are not already numbered (as they would be in a federal complaint), reference the page number so your reader can avoid the unnecessary task of counting paragraphs for several pages until she reaches the material cited.

     Def.'s Br. Support Mot. Summ. J. 14

The final element of the document citation is the date parenthetical. Rule 25.2(c) requires the full date, with the month abbreviated according to Appendix 3. The general rule with regard to the date is to provide the most "official" date possible. Therefore, if the document is filed with the court, provide the date of filing. If it is not filed with the court, provide the date the document was served on opposing counsel, which should be the date on the certificate of service.[1] If the document was neither filed nor served, use the date the document was prepared. If none of these dates can be determined, include the abbreviation "n.d." in the date parenthetical.

With regard to formatting document citations, notice that citations to court documents, unlike citations to authority, may be formatted in bold type, included in parentheses, or both. Although all three are correct, the ICW will expect the document cites, like those in the ALWD Guide's examples, to be not enclosed in parentheses or in bold typeface.

---

[1] If the date on the certificate of service is *not* the actual date of service, use the actual date of service for the citation.

Pl.'s Mot. Directed Verdict ¶ 4, Mar. 12, 2004.

Rule 25.3 provides a specific citation form for trial, hearing, or deposition transcripts. The format is very similar to the form for other court documents. The citation starts with the abbreviated transcript name and ends with the date on which the transcribed proceeding occurred. In the pinpoint reference, though, the citation form makes a few modifications to account for the differences between typed documents and transcribed testimony.

The first difference between typed documents and transcribed testimony is that every line of transcribed testimony is numbered for easy reference to specific statements. The second difference is that transcribed testimony is often so lengthy that it must be divided into multiple volumes. For example, a single deposition may be divided into three volumes of transcribed testimony. Therefore, the pinpoint reference identifies both the page and line number(s) of the testimony cited as well as the volume number if the transcript is divided into multiple volumes.

Dep. John Carter 75:18, Dec. 5, 2003.

Dep. William Claxton vol. 4, 163:2, Feb. 2, 2004.

2. Short Citation Form

Rule 25.4 tells you not to use "*id.*" unless the name of the document is extremely long. If "*id.*" is not appropriate, Rule 25.4 tells you to create the short form of a document citation by referring to individual's by their surnames and by omitting the date.

| | Def.'s Br. Support Mot. Summ. J. 39, Oct. 31, 2003. |
| becomes: | Def.'s Br. Support Mot. Summ. J. 39. |

| | Aff. Jan W. Bryant ¶ 9, Nov. 3, 2003. |
| becomes: | Aff. Bryant ¶ 9. |

B. CITING DOCUMENTS ON APPEAL

When a case begins the appellate process, documents filed with the trial court clerk's office are referred to as part of the record ("R.") rather than as individual documents (*e.g.*, "Pl.'s Mot. Compel"). The documents in the clerk's file are consecutively numbered, beginning with the complaint and ending with the last document in the case. At that point, all material is referenced by page number rather than paragraph number. A line number may be added to the pinpoint reference for clarity. Therefore, the Complaint might have been cited like this during the course of the trial:

Pl.'s Compl. ¶ 3, July 25, 2003.

However, when the parties refer to the Complaint in the appellate briefs, it would be cited like this:

(R. at 1:14.)[2]

---

[2] Rule 25.5 gives you the option of formatting the record cite in a number of ways. The ICW exercise will look for a format consistent with this example: (R. at pg:line.)

And there you have it! For the record, you're ready for the exercise!

Exercise 16
COURT DOCUMENTS

Put the following information in correct *ALWD* citation form. All cases are being cited in citation sentences in a brief to a federal district court. This exercise focuses on Rule 25. You will also need to refer to Appendix 3 for abbreviations of words commonly used in court document titles. You should enclose the entire citation in parentheses. You should use "*id.*" where it would be permissible to do so, even if the document name is not long.

1. In a Motion in Limine, you wish to cite page 3 of the November 5, 2019, affidavit of Meredith Grey, M.D. To date in this litigation, Dr. Grey has only sworn one affidavit.

_____

_____

_____

2. Without any intervening cites, you again want to cite to page 3 of Dr. Grey's November 5, 2019, affidavit. Assume that the name of the document is not extremely long.

_____

_____

_____

3. In the same Motion in Limine mentioned in #1 and #2, you wish to cite to paragraph 13 of the Defendant's Second Amended Answer, prepared on July 15, 2019, served on July 16, 2019, and filed on July 16, 2019. [Assume a date would be helpful.]

_____

_____

_____

4. In a Motion for Summary Judgment, you wish to cite to paragraph 3 of Plaintiff's Complaint, prepared on July 1, 2019, served on July 3, 2019, and filed on July 2, 2019. [Assume a date would be helpful.]

_____

_____

_____

5. In a Motion for Protective Order, you wish to cite page 3 of Defendant's Request for Production, prepared on August 6, 2019, and served on August 6, 2019. To date in this litigation, the Defendant has only filed one Request for Production.

_____

_____

_____

6. In a Motion for New Trial, you wish to cite the testimony of Christina Yang, M.D., Ph.D. Her testimony begins in volume 1 of the trial transcript. You wish to cite her testimony beginning on line 2 of page 75 and ending with line 20 of page 75. The testimony was given on September 10, 2020.

_____

_____

7. Two paragraphs later, in the same motion, you wish to cite to Harrison Cole's deposition testimony at page 7, line 18 to page 9, line 14. Mr. Cole gave his testimony on December 3, 2019. You want to use the word "to" to avoid confusion.

_____

_____

_____

8. On page 8 of an appellate brief, you wish to cite to the judge's denial of the Motion for New Trial. In the consecutively numbered record kept by the court clerk, the order denying the Motion for New Trial is on page 537. Assume that Court rules require that citations to the appellate records be enclosed in parentheses.

_____

_____

_____

Chapter 17

LAW REVIEW FOOTNOTES

INTRODUCTION

The first sixteen chapters have taught you how to construct citations to be used in office memoranda and legal documents. As a practicing attorney, the vast majority of the writing you will do will be in one of these two categories. However, as a law student writing seminar papers and short articles for law journals, you will need to learn the citation form that is used for citations in scholarly legal writing. This third category of writing encompasses various forms of writing that are found in academic journals: notes, comments, book reviews and full-length articles. Most law school seminar papers are also required to follow this format, as well as most articles found in bar journals and other legal publications.

If you have written extensively in an undergraduate or graduate program, you know that each academic discipline follows citations rules, as to both substance and form, found in publication manuals for that discipline. For example, many liberal arts graduate programs require research papers to conform to the *MLA Handbook for Writers of Research Papers* (the "MLA"), and social science programs commonly adopt the *Publication Manual of the American Psychological Association* (the "APA"). In law schools, most upper-level writing requirements are satisfied by an academic paper whose citations conform to the *Bluebook* and the *ALWD Guide*, and most law-related academic publications require article submissions to conform to the *Bluebook* and the *ALWD Guide* as well.

As mentioned before, the *ALWD Guide* has slightly different rules, mostly typeface conventions, for citations that appear in court documents and legal memoranda and for those that appear in scholarly articles. Therefore, this chapter will enable you to construct academic citations, which we will refer to loosely as "law review citations," from the knowledge you have gained using the preceding chapters of the ICW. Although the other chapters of this book have prepared you for the kinds of writing you have done in a first-year legal research and writing course or in an internship at a law office or other type of legal employment, this chapter will teach you the skills necessary to participate in a journal writing competition, write a seminar paper and prepare a note or comment for a law school journal.

A. CITATION PLACEMENT

One major difference between citations in legal documents and memoranda and law review citations is that law review citations are never embedded in the text; law review citations appear in footnotes, signaled by a superscript numeral, called a "footnote call number," after the clause or sentence that requires the citation (Rule 34.1(e)(FN)). The footnote call number appears after most punctuation marks, but before colons and dashes (Rule 34.1(e)(2)(FN)). The citation sentence then appears in the footnote itself. Nonetheless, law review citations are still full sentences that begin with a capital letter and end with a period (Rule 34.1(e)(2)(FN)).

Unlike in the days of typewriters when creating footnotes entailed much planning and a little math, creating footnotes using a word processing program is incredibly simple and much more helpful than endnotes. In WordPerfect, you "Insert" a "Footnote." In Word, you "Insert" a "Reference," then "Footnote." At least one notable legal commentator has suggested using footnotes in all types of legal documents,[1] particularly documents submitted to courts, but so far footnotes are not widely used in law practice.

B. TYPEFACE CONVENTIONS

The first difference you will notice in creating law review citations is that, in law review citations, parts of citations may be in plain type, LARGE AND SMALL CAPITALS, or *italics* (Rule 1.4). Large and small capitals are easily produced using your word processing software: in both Word and WordPerfect, this function is called "small caps" under the "Font" heading. In addition to adding the small caps typeface to statute citations and secondary source citations, law review citations also change the typeface conventions you have learned in certain types of citations, such as case names.

1. Case Names

For full and short citations of cases in legal documents and memoranda, you italicized the case name. However, in law review citations, the case name is not italicized when using the full citation form, only the short form (Rule 12.2(a)(2)(FN)).

Therefore,

    United States v. Grass, 239 F. Supp. 2d 535 (M.D. Pa. 2003).

becomes

    United States v. Grass, 239 F. Supp. 2d 535 (M.D. Pa. 2003).

The acceptable short forms for this case would be identical under the law review citations rules as under the rules for legal documents and memoranda. For example,

    Grass, 239 F. Supp. 2d at 546.

or

    Id. at 546.

2. Statutes

For legal documents and memoranda, you produced the name of the statutory compilation in plain type, whether the statute was found in the *United States Code* or a state publication, such as the *California Corporations Code*. However, in law review citations, the name of the statutory compilation appears in small caps (Rule 14.4(c)(FN)).

---

[1] *See* BRYAN A. GARNER, THE WINNING BRIEF 139–47 (2d ed. 2004).

Therefore,

Tex. Penal Code Ann. § 12.32(a) (West 2007).

becomes

Tᴇx. Pᴇɴᴀʟ Cᴏᴅᴇ Aɴɴ. § 12.32(a) (West 2007).

Because the abbreviation for the *United States Code* is all capital letters, "U.S.C.," the difference in typeface from plain type to small caps is irrelevant.

Note that if you wanted to give the name of a particular statutory act or provision, then that name would still appear in plain type.

This typeface change also applies to specialized statutes covered by Rule 162, such as rules of evidence and procedure (Rule 16.1(f)(FN)) and Rule 23, such as restatements, model codes, and sentencing guidelines (Rules 23.1(e)(FN), 23.5(c)(FN), and 23.4(b)(FN)).

Therefore,

Fed. R. Civ. P. 31.

becomes

Fᴇᴅ. R. Cɪv. P. 31.

Again, because citations to the statutory tax provisions found in the Internal Revenue Code (Rule 14.2(h)(FN)) use the all-capital abbreviation "I.R.C.," this typeface change is irrelevant.

3. Legislative, Administrative, and Executive Materials

The differences in typeface between legal documents and scholarly articles are less focused with regard to the various types of legislative materials. The law review citation format for legislative bills and resolutions are the same as for legal documents, as well as citations to the *Federal Register* and the *Code of Federal Regulations*. In addition, citations to executive orders and presidential papers remain in plain type. However, for federal reports from the House of Representatives and the Senate, part of the citation is in small caps (Rule 15.7(g)(FN)). In addition, citations to the *Congressional Record* abbreviate the title of that publication using small caps (Rule 15.10(a)(6)(FN)).

Therefore,

H.R. Rep. No. 104-83 (1999).

becomes

H.R. Rᴇᴘ. Nᴏ. 104-83 (1999).

and

143 Cong. Rec. H12,345 (daily ed. Apr. 14, 1999).

becomes

143 Cᴏɴɢ. Rᴇᴄ. H12,345 (daily ed. Apr. 14, 1999).

4.　Secondary Sources

In writing seminar papers and other academic articles, you will cite to many more secondary sources than you have previously in writing memoranda, appellate briefs and court motions for your other classes. When practitioners write to each other and to the court, they are attempting to explain what the current state of the law is, citing to primary authority such as statutes and cases. Only when the law does not fully contemplate the situation at hand do practitioners and courts then turn to persuasive authority such as law review articles, treatises and books. However, scholarly writers, who are commonly arguing for a change in an existing legal paradigm, cite to secondary authority frequently. Perhaps understandably, the law review citation form for these types of sources differs from the citation form used in legal documents.

Both the author and title of a book appear in small caps (Rule 20.1(f)(FN)). The names of editors, translators, and publishers remain in plain type (Rule 20.1(f)(FN)).

Therefore,

Frederick Lewis Allen, *Only Yesterday* (1931).

becomes

FREDERICK LEWIS ALLEN, ONLY YESTERDAY (1931).

Shorter works such as articles and works in a collection still appear with the author's name in plain type and the title of the work in italics, but the name of the collection or periodical appears in small caps.

Therefore,

Lisa M. Fairfax, *Martha Stewart and Director Independence, in Martha Stewart's Legal Troubles* 359 (Joan MacLeod Heminway ed., 2007).

becomes

Lisa M. Fairfax, *Martha Stewart and Director Independence, in* MARTHA STEWART'S LEGAL TROUBLES 359 (Joan MacLeod Heminway ed., 2007).

and

Ann Althouse, *Why a Narrowly Defined Legal Scholarship Blog Is Not What I Want: An Argument in Pseudo-blog Form*, 84 Wash. U. L. Rev. 1221 (2006).

becomes

Ann Althouse, *Why a Narrowly Defined Legal Scholarship Blog Is Not What I Want: An Argument in Pseudo-blog Form*, 84 WASH. U. L. REV. 1221 (2006).

Finally,

Kristen Hays, *No Fanfare as Skilling Steps into Prison Life*, Hous. Chron., Dec. 14, 2006, at A1.

becomes

Kristen Hays, *No Fanfare as Skilling Steps into Prison Life*, HOUS. CHRON., Dec. 14, 2006, at A1.

5. Electronic Sources

The core of an electronic source citation is borrowed from the citation form for the underlying source. For example, an electronic source citation for a case contains the same typeface conventions as a case citation, and so does a statute citation, etc. Therefore, when creating an electronic source citation in a law review footnote, review the typeface conventions for the underlying source.

Tex. Penal Code § 12.32(a) (Westlaw through 2017 Reg. Sess.).

Typeface Differences

	Legal Memoranda or Document	Scholarly Article
case	*Rutherford v. Chrysler Motors Corp.*, 231 N.W.2d 413 (Mich. Ct. App. 1975).	Rutherford v. Chrysler Motors Corp., 231 N.W.2d 413 (Mich. Ct. App. 1975).
case short form	*Rutherford*, 231 N.W.2d at 415.	*Rutherford*, 231 N.W.2d at 415.
statute	Ariz. Rev. Stat. § 17-454 (2007).	ARIZ. REV. STAT. § 17-454 (2007).
statute short form	Ariz. Rev. Stat. § 17-455.	ARIZ. REV. STAT. § 17-455.
rule	Model Rules of Prof'l Conduct R. 8.4(d) (2003).	MODEL RULES OF PROF'L CONDUCT R. 8.4(d) (2003).
article	William J. Stuntz, *The Pathological Politics of the Criminal Law*, 100 Mich. L. Rev. 505 (2001).	William J. Stuntz, *The Pathological Politics of the Criminal Law*, 100 MICH. L. REV. 505 (2001).
newspaper	John Kass, *Governor Has One Choice Left*, Chi. Trib., Dec. 9, 2008, at A7.	John Kass, *Governor Has One Choice Left*, CHI. TRIB., Dec. 9, 2008, at A7.
book	Henry G. Manne, *Insider Trading and the Stock Market* (1966).	HENRY G. MANNE, INSIDER TRADING AND THE STOCK MARKET (1966).
congressional report	H.R. Rep. No. 110-210, at 23 (2007).	H.R. REP. No. 110-210, at 23 (2007).
congressional debate	154 Cong. Rec. 10,793 (2008).	154 CONG. REC. 10,793 (2008).
electronic source	*United States v. Bajakajian*, 524 U.S. 321 (1998), http://supct.law.cornell.edu/supct/cases/name.htm.	United States v. Bajakajian, 524 U.S. 321 (1998), http://supct.law.cornell.edu/supct/cases/name.htm.
direct citation to electronic source	Sarah Hepola, *My Big, Fat, Unpaid Credit Card Bill*, Salon.com, Jan. 30, 2008, http://salon.com/mwt/feature/2008/01/30/credit_card_debt/.	Sarah Hepola, *My Big, Fat, Unpaid Credit Card Bill*, SALON.COM, Jan. 30, 2008, http://salon.com/mwt/feature/2008/01/30/credit_card_debt/.

C. PARALLEL CITATIONS

In earlier chapters, you learned to construct parallel citations for state cases if required by the local rules. In these parallel citations, readers would be referred not only to a West regional reporter, but also to an official state reporter or a public domain citation. In scholarly writing, however, the audience is intended to be national, even international. Therefore, local rules are irrelevant and scholarly works generally do not contain parallel citations. For state cases in your article or note, merely cite to a regional reporter unless told otherwise by a particular legal publication.

D. SIGNALS AND PARENTHETICALS

When writing for your first-year legal writing class, you probably used a few signals in the court documents and legal memoranda you prepared. Because you were using mostly primary authority, you probably used *"see," "see also"* and *"but see"* more than any others and may have used few of those signals. However, once you begin writing academic papers that make arguments about what the law should be, and not just what the law is, then you may begin to cite to secondary sources that require a signal to reflect the relationship between your assertion and the substance of the cited source. In addition, you will probably be using more parentheticals to assist you in showing your reader the relevance of a particular secondary source. If you become an editor for a law journal, or have an article edited by a law journal, you will find that many journals have their own policies regarding signals, parentheticals and even the types of gerunds that may appear in a parenthetical. The *ICW* has earlier chapters on the use of signals and parentheticals, and those rules apply with even more force to academic writing. Please review those chapters if you would like help in using signals or constructing parentheticals.

E. SHORT FORM REFERENCES AND INTERNAL REFERENCES

In previous chapters, we've discussed the use of *"id."* to reference both cases and statutes that have been cited in the same general discussion in legal documents. Rule 11.3 tells us that *"id."* may be used to cite "any kind of authority except internal cross-references." Therefore, we can use *"id."* to refer to books, articles, legislative history and other types of sources if that source appears in the immediately preceding citation within the same footnote or in the previous footnote, when the previous footnote contains only one source.

We have also discussed how to create a short form for books and cases for situations in which you want to formulate a short form for a source that has been cited previously, but not in the immediately preceding citation. Previous chapters have not discussed short forms for other sources, such as secondary sources, that are commonly cited in scholarly works. For these situations, Rule 11.4 tells us to use *"supra"* and "hereinafter" "to refer to legislative hearings; books; pamphlets; reports; unpublished materials; nonprint resources; periodicals; services; treaties and international agreements; regulations, directives, and decisions of intergovernmental organizations; and internal cross- references" but not for "cases, statutes, constitutions, legislative materials (other than hearings), restatements, model codes, or regulations."

1. Cases and Statutes

When referring to a source cited in the immediately preceding citation, you may still use *"id."* in your law review footnote. Rule 11.3 tells us to use *"id."* when citing the immediately preceding authority within the same footnote or within the immediately preceding footnote *when the preceding footnote contains only one authority.*

If you cannot use *"id."* and must compose an acceptable short form, then Rules 12.16(g)(FN) (Cases) and 14.5(b)(FN) (Statutes) provide the forms for law review citations. Although the short forms are generally the same, note that both these Rules provide an additional limitation on the use of short forms in academic writings with footnotes, which may be much longer than legal memoranda and may discuss various topics. In these types of writings, you may use a short form to clearly identify a case or statute that "is already cited in the *same footnote*" or "is cited *in any of the preceding five footnotes*."

The purpose of this rule is to enable a reader to easily find a full citation either on the same page that the reader is reading text or on the page or so before it. Given that law review articles have grown so long that some law reviews have begun imposing word limits of 30,000 or fewer on submissions, this rule can save a reader from having to thumb through pages and pages of text in search of a full citation. Therefore, if you have not referred to a case or statute in the previous five footnotes, you will have to provide your reader with a full citation for that source again.

2. Secondary Sources, "*Supra*," and "Hereinafter"

Again, you may still use "*id.*" in citation footnotes to refer to any type of secondary source, such as a book or periodical article, when the source was cited in the immediately preceding citation. However, if you cannot use "*id.*," then you must refer to the previous secondary source citation using the "*supra*" format as a short form citation (Rule 11.4(d)(FN)). This type of short form generally refers to the source by using the author's last name and a reference back to the numbered footnote in which the full citation appears. The citation will also include any type of pinpoint information. The typeface for the author's name will match the typeface used in the original full citation. If the source is a journal article, then the author's name will appear in plain type both in the full citation and the supra short form. However, if the source is a book, then the author's name will appear in small caps in both footnote citations. If the work has more than one author, then use all the authors' names in the supra short form if all authors' names were used in the original citation.

Author, *supra* note X, at Y.

or, if a book

AUTHOR, *supra* note X, at Y.

A comma separates the author's name from the word "supra" in italics, then the word "note" appears in plain type and then the footnote number. Any pinpoint will appear at the end, preceded by a comma and, if the pinpoint is to a page number, the word "at" (Rule 11.4(e)(FN)).

[3] JAMES D. COX & THOMAS LEE HAZEN, CORPORATIONS (2003).

[4] *See* Larry E. Ribstein, *Fraud on a Noisy Market*, 10 LEWIS & CLARK L. REV. 137 (2006).

[5] *See* COX & HAZEN, *supra* note 3, at 420 (explaining the difference between a direct, individual suit and a derivative action).

[6] *Id.* at 421.

[7] *See* Ribstein, *supra* note 4, at 155 (noting also that if the market is "noisy" or irrational, damages are even more difficult to attribute to disclosures of fraud).

If the work has no author, then the *supra* form should refer to first piece of information in the citation, usually the title.

[43] TORTS STORIES (Robert L. Rabin & Stephen D. Sugarman, eds., 2003).

[44] United States v. Carroll Towing Co., 159 F.2d 169 (2d Cir. 1947).

[45] TORTS STORIES, *supra* note 43.

If in your paper you cite to more than one source by a particular author or author group, you must devise a system for distinguishing *supra* forms for the various works. When the two sources appear in the same footnote, distinguishing the sources by something other than footnote number is mandatory for the *supra* short form to work. However, even when two sources by the same author appear in different numbered footnotes, creating a nickname for the sources can also aid your reader. The "hereinafter" device can work well in both situations (Rule 11.5(c)(FN)). Formulate a shorthand title for each work and use "hereinafter" to label the works as such. In the original citation to the source, at the end of the citation but before any explanatory parenthetical, insert within brackets the word "hereinafter" and the chosen nickname. The words in the nickname appear in the same typeface used for those words in the original citation. The word "hereinafter" appears in plain type.

Then, in subsequent *supra* short forms, use that abbreviated title in connection with the author's name. The hereinafter nickname should appear in the same typeface as whichever part of the full citation it is abbreviating.

[4] Larry E. Ribstein, *Fraud on a Noisy Market*, 10 LEWIS & CLARK L. REV. 137 (2006) [hereinafter Ribstein, *Noisy Market*].

[5] *See* COX & HAZEN, *supra* note 3, at 420 (explaining the difference between a direct, individual suit and a derivative action).

[6] *Id.* at 421.

[7] *See* Ribstein, *Noisy Market, supra* note 4, at 155 (noting also that if the market is "noisy" or irrational, then damages are even more difficult to attribute to disclosures of fraud).

"Hereinafter" is also a useful tool when a normal *supra* short form would be long or cumbersome, for example, when a source has no author but a lengthy title, such as hearings, regulatory filings and various types of reports. Creating a shorthand nickname for a source can also be useful when the source is well known by a particular name.

[18] ATTORNEY GENERAL'S COMMISSION ON PORNOGRAPHY, FINAL REPORT (1986) [hereinafter MEESE REPORT].

[19] *Unlawful Internet Gambling Funding Prohibition Act and the Internet Gambling Licensing and Regulation Commission Act: Hearing on H.R. 21 and H.R. 1223 Before the Subcomm. on Crime, Terrorism, and Homeland Security of the H. Comm. on the Judiciary*, 108th Cong. 8-12 (2003) [hereinafter 2003 Hearing].

[20] NATIONAL GAMBLING IMPACT STUDY COMM'N, FINAL REPORT (1999) [hereinafter "NGISC REPORT"].

[21] *See* MEESE REPORT, *supra* note 18, at 5.

3. Internal Cross-References

Because most legal documents you have written so far have been fairly short, you may not have needed to refer in your text either to a prior discussion or a future discussion within the same writing. In lengthy academic writing, referring to another portion of the same article is quite common, for example, when you want to mention a possible area of concern that you intend to cover in greater detail later in the same article. To alert your reader that you realize this assertion requires authority and that further discussion will satisfy that requirement, you can simply create a footnote that cites to that section of the article, whether it is a textual section or a footnote or group of footnotes. If the cited section appears prior to your textual sentence, use "*supra*," if after, use "*infra*" (Rule 10.2(a)(FN)). The portion of the article to which you are referring appears in plain type, with no commas.

Although this type of cross-reference can be useful and save writers from repeating themselves, writers can be tempted to insert too many cross-references. Although there are no hard and fast rules, be aware if you are repeatedly referring to sections that appear later in your paper. Your paper could benefit from being reorganized if you are concerned that your reader will not understand one section without referring to a later section. On the other hand, you may merely be inserting unnecessary cross-references.

F. NEW TYPES OF SOURCES

One thing you will note in writing your first seminar paper or law journal piece is that you will be citing from a more varied set of sources. Although the *ICW* has taught you how to cite to the most frequently cited sources, such as cases, statutes, constitutions, regulations, books and law review articles, you will occasionally need to cite to a source and not know where to begin in formulating a citation form. The best place to begin with the *ALWD Guide* is with the index, which is fairly thorough, if not exhaustive. A quick glance at the "B" entries reveals entries for *Black's Law Dictionary*, blogs, BNA publications, broadcasts, and books and pamphlets such as ABA publications.

Of course, no matter how often the *ALWD Guide* is updated or how thorough the index is, every paper will have a source that does not seem to match exactly to a current *ALWD Guide* rule. When this happens, use your judgment and find a rule that addresses a source similar to the source you need to cite and adapt the citation format.

For example, imagine that you are writing a paper on legal issues arising in space law, particularly in abandoned space equipment orbiting the earth. You want to make the assertion that space law is a growing field and want to cite to a three-day conference at a well known law school as evidence of that assertion. The conference does not have a website at the time of your writing, but you do have a "Save the Date" postcard from the law school announcing the upcoming conference. Consulting the index, you see there are no entries for "postcard," "brochure," "press release," "invitation" or "announcement." However, you notice there are rules for "pamphlets," "leaflets," and "letters." The rule that seems like it might work is Rule 27 for interviews, letters, and memoranda. So, you try to adapt the format something like this, using the date you received the mailing:

Announcement, Elite College of Law, Join Us at the Third Annual Space Law Conference, March 3-5, 2010 (Jan. 10, 2009) (on file with author).

Good luck!

Exercise 17
LAW REVIEW FOOTNOTES

For this set of exercises, you will revisit citation forms that you know: cases, statutes, legislative and administrative sources, and secondary sources. You know the basic format of sources under the ALWD Rules, but now you will use the rules and typefaces pertaining to law reviews.

For purposes of these exercises, create the citation that would go into a footnote in an academic article following the typeface conventions and rules for law reviews. All sources are being cited in academic footnotes. Although most footnote citations in academic articles begin with some sort of signal, for purposes of these exercises, do not include a signal unless one is provided for you.

Note: When using the large and small caps emphasis, please highlight *as a single unit* the text you want to appear in large and small caps rather than highlighting each word individually. For example, in the citation "123 Harv. L. Rev. 456", you should highlight "Harv. L. Rev." as a single unit and then click on the large and small caps button. Do not include text that does not belong in large and small caps, such as "123" and "456".

LAW REVIEW: CASE CITATIONS

1. L.M. Dennis versus Nelson Gary, a case from the Supreme Court of Washington, decided November 30, 1909, and reported at volume 105, page 172, of *Pacific Reporter*.

2. Jacqueline Suzanne Agathe Jagiella, a/k/a Jacqueline Regaux Jagiella, versus Waclav James Constantine Jagiella, a/k/a Waclav J. Jagiella, a case decided by the United States Court of Appeals for the Fifth Circuit, Unit B, on June 11, 1981, and reported at volume 647, page 561, of *Federal Reporter*, Second Series.

3. Robert Shannon versus Union Pacific Railway Company, a case from the Supreme Court of Kansas, decided February 11, 1888, and reported at volume 16, page 836, of *Pacific Reporter*.

4. The Brotherhood of American Yeomen, defendant-appellant, versus Mrs. Mina Graves, plaintiff-appellee, a case decided by the Court of Appeals of Kentucky, which was the highest state court in that state until 1976. This particular case was decided April 29, 1930, and reported at volume 27, page 670, of *South Western Reporter*, Second Series.

_____

_____

5. Food Lion, Incorporated versus United Food and Commercial Workers International Union, et al. and United Steelworkers of America, et al., a case decided by the United States Court of Appeals in the District of Columbia on January 10, 1997, after oral arguments on November 21, 1996. The case is reported at volume 103, page 1007, of *Federal Reporter*, Third Series.

_____

_____

LAW REVIEW: STATE AND FEDERAL STATUTES

1. Article three, section two, clause 2 of the Constitution of the United States.

_____

_____

2. Section 10A-1-6.31 of the *Code of Alabama*, 1975, published by West. This new provision appears entirely in the 2018 bound volume.

_____

_____

3. Subsections (a)(1) through (a)(7) of section 113 of title 18 of the current *United States Code*, published in 2012.

_____

_____

_____

4. Sections 11-9-650 through 11-9-660 of the *Code of Laws of South Carolina 1976 Annotated*, published by West. Part of this citation appears in the 2011 main volume, and part appears in the 2019 cumulative supplement. Using a dash to separate the span of sections would be ambiguous.

_____

_____

_____

5. Subsection (b)(2)(A) of section 1070a of title 20 of the current United States Code, published in Supplement V in 2017.

_____

_____

_____

6. The current Rule 4(a) of the Federal Rules of Appellate Procedure, published in 2012 in the Appendix to title 28 of the *United States Code*.

_____

_____

_____

LAW REVIEW: LEGISLATIVE AND ADMINISTRATIVE SOURCES

1. You wish to cite to a June 29, 1999 conference report on H.R. 775. The report was given a House report number of 106-212. The relevant portion appears in part 3. The report was not published in U.S.C.C.A.N.

_____

_____

_____

2. You want to refer to some testimony made during a committee hearing in front of the House Committee on Education and the Workforce on September 21, 2000. The title of the hearing is "The National and Economic Importance of Improving Math-Science Education and H.R. 4272, the National Science Education Enhancement Act." The remarks were made by Rep. Vernon J. Ehlers on page 30. The hearing was during the 106th Congress.

_____

_____

_____

3. You wish to cite a statement of Senator Russell Finegold that was made on the floor of the Senate on July 10, 2001, on the death penalty. The transcript of this debate is found in the permanent edition of the *Congressional Record*, volume 147, page 7418.

_____

_____

4. In a discussion of the legislative history of the Truth in Lending Act, you cite a session law called the Truth in Lending Class Action Relief Act, published in volume 109 of *United States Statutes at Large* on page 161. The law was codified as section 1640 of title 15 of the *United States Code*. The bill was passed in April of 1995 and given the public law number 104-12.

_____

_____

5. In a discussion of the legislative history of certain laws passed following the attacks on the World Trade Center and the Pentagon on September 11, 2001, you wish to cite a session law called the United and Strengthening America by Providing Appropriate Tools Required to Intercept and Obstruct Terrorism (USA Patriot Act) Act of 2001, published in volume 115 of the *United States Statutes at Large* on page 272. The bill was the 56th bill passed by both houses of Congress in October of 2001 during the 107th Congress. This act is known as the "USA Patriot Act."

_____

_____

6. Draft the citation for the regulations implementing the National Voting Registration Act, 42 U.S.C. § 1973gg-1 (1994). The regulations are found in title 11 of the 2019 edition of the *Code of Federal Regulations*, sections 8.3 through 8.6.

_____

_____

7. You are writing on the history of OSHA, and you want to cite to Executive Order No. 12196, signed by President James E. Carter on February 26, 1980. This order is found at 1980 U.S.C.C.A.N. 7696 and in volume 45 of the *Federal Register*, page 12,769. It is not published in the *Code of Federal Regulations*.

_____

_____

_____

LAW REVIEW: SECONDARY SOURCES

1. "The Future of Reputation," a book published in 2007 by the Yale University Press. The author is Daniel J. Solove. You want to focus your reader's attention on page 5.

_____

_____

_____

2. "Superfreakonomics," a book by Steven D. Levitt and Stephen J. Dubner, published in 2009 by William Morrow.

_____

_____

_____

3. An article by Lyrissa Barnett Lidsky entitled "Silencing John Doe: Defamation and Discourse in Cyberspace," published beginning on page 855 of volume 49 of the Duke Law Journal in 2000.

_____

_____

_____

4. A newspaper article by Matthew Goldstein, Ben Protess, and Andrew Ross Sorkin entitled "Hedge Fund Sues U.S. Prosecutor." This article appeared at A1 of the New York Times on February 26, 2015. For ease of access, you would like to also direct your reader to the URL where the article can be found, http://www.nytimes.com/2015/02/27/business/dealbook/fbi-warrant-in-insider-trading-cases-is-unsealed.html.

_____

_____

_____

5. An article by Larry Ribstein entitled "The Death of Big Law." This 2010 article appeared in volume 2010 of the Wisconsin Law Review beginning on page 749. You wish to direct your reader's attention to page 801 of this article.

_____

_____

_____

6. "To Love & To Cherish," an article by Pamela Colloff about the fight for gay marriage in Texas. It is in volume 43, issue 3, of Texas Monthly, a nonconsecutively paginated magazine. The article, published in 2015, begins on page 86.

LAW REVIEW: SHORT FORMS

1. In the introduction of your case comment, you mentioned a book by Kent Greenawalt and provided a citation in your eighth footnote, "KENT GREENAWALT, SPEECH, CRIME AND THE USE OF LANGUAGE (1989)." Now, in the third section of your article, you wish to create a citation for use in a footnote that refers back to page 103 of this book.

---

2. A few sentences earlier, you cited to a law review article by Douglas A. Kysar and provided a citation in your one hundred twenty-third footnote, "Douglas A. Kysar, *The Expectations of Consumers*, 103 COLUM. L. REV. 1700 (2003)." Now, after several intervening cites, you wish to create a citation for use in your one hundred thirtieth footnote that refers back to page 1738 of this article.

---

3. In your article you will be referring to several articles by Lucinda M. Finley. The first article was published in 1998 and is entitled "The Hidden Victims of Tort Reform: Women, Children, and the Elderly." It appears in volume 53 of the Emory Law Journal at page 1263. You know that you will be citing to this article numerous times, as well as other articles by Professor Finley. To distinguish this article from the others, you want to refer to it as "Hidden Victims." Create an original citation for this article for use in your footnote twenty-four, including a hereinafter nickname that you will reference in later footnotes.

---

4. In a later footnote, you wish to refer back to the Finley article in your footnote twenty-four and direct your reader to pages 1270 through 1272.

---

5. In your fifteenth footnote, you created a citation to a famous case from the Court of Appeals of New York, *Palsgraf v. Long Island Railroad Company*, which appeared in volume 162 of the Northeastern Reporter, page 99, in 1928. You now want to cite to page 100 of this case. Create the appropriate citation for your thirtieth footnote.

_____

_____

_____

6. In footnote thirty-three, after several citations to *Overseas Tankership (U.K.) Ltd.*, you wish to cite again to page 101 of *Palsgraf*. Create the citation.

_____

_____

_____

7. A few pages earlier in your academic article, you cited to a Colorado statute, section 13-21-403, from the *Colorado Revised Statutes Annotated*, published by West in 2009. Now, after many intervening cites, you wish to cite to the statute section again. Create the citation.

_____

_____

_____

8. Two footnotes later, you wish to cite to this provision again. Use the option listed in example footnote 90 in 14.5(b) to create the citation.

_____

_____

_____

9. In the introduction to your seminar paper, you wish to give an overview of your paper's thesis and analysis. In doing so, you make the assertion that the Socratic method has never been empirically tested to be a superior form of information delivery than other classroom methods. You realize that this assertion needs support and therefore want to direct your reader to this assertion in Part IV of your paper. Create the citation for a footnote to this controversial assertion about the Socratic method using the signal "see."

_____

_____

_____

10. Later, you decide that you want to direct your reader to particular foot noted authorities that appear earlier in your paper, specifically in footnotes 80-92. These footnotes contain citation sentences, but no textual sentences. Create this citation, using the signal "see."
